Our American Holidays

THANKSGIVING

OUR AMERICAN HOLIDAYS
Edited by Robert Haven Schauffler

FLAG DAY
CHRISTMAS
ARBOR DAY
MOTHERS' DAY
THANKSGIVING
MEMORIAL DAY
INDEPENDENCE DAY
LINCOLN'S BIRTHDAY
WASHINGTON'S BIRTHDAY

For brief description of each volume see
advertisement facing last page of text.

THANKSGIVING

ITS ORIGIN, CELEBRATION
AND SIGNIFICANCE AS RE-
LATED IN PROSE AND VERSE

382

EDITED BY

ROBERT HAVEN SCHAUFFLER

NEW YORK
MOFFAT, YARD & COMPANY
1916

NOTE

The selections from the works of James Russell Lowell, John G. Whittier, Jane G. Austin and Kate Douglas Wiggin, are used by special permission of Messrs. Houghton, Mifflin & Company. We also wish to extend our thanks to Messrs. Little, Brown & Co., The Century Co., *The Youth's Companion,* and others who have kindly allowed us to reprint selections from works bearing their copyright.

CONTENTS

CONTENTS

CONTENTS

THANKSGIVING.

PREFACE.

Every autumn in school and home recurs the
need for a collection of literature on Thanksgiving,— an anthology comprehensive enough
to include all the best that has been written
about this intensely American holiday. For
years the imperative ungratified demand for
such a book has almost suggested a dark conspiracy among literary folk,— a conspiracy
which the present volume is intended to
thwart. It brings to children of all ages all
the best poems, essays, plays and stories of
Thanksgiving. And its scope is yet wider.

The Introduction gives a rapid view of the
holiday's origin, its derivation from ancient festivals; its development, its spirit and its significance. This part of the book endeavors to
be as suggestive as possible to parents and
teachers who are personally conducted to the
sources for the study of their subject.

INTRODUCTION

I
ORIGIN

THANKSGIVING

THANKSGIVING IN AMERICA

MAY LOWE

Thanksgiving Day, as instituted in New England, may have gained an impetus in the fact that while the Pilgrims lived at Leyden (they having quitted England for Holland, where they lived ten years,) they were wont to observe the manner in which their Dutch friends celebrated, on October 3rd, their deliverance from the Spaniards. This was the most popular festival of the Dutch, except the Kirmess, and was kept as both a religious and a social holiday, though it soon degenerated into merely a day of merriment. The chief dish at dinner upon that day was a Spanish hodge-podge, a stew of meat and vegetables.

After observing for ten years this Thanksgiving Day in Holland, it is small wonder that after the Pilgrims had come to America, they should establish a time of thanksgiving and rejoicing for their first harvest, which had yielded well.

After leaving Holland, they had a perilous voyage, but at last, after many dangers and hardships, they landed, on December 21st,

1620, on Plymouth Rock. Until such time as they might build houses and establish themselves upon the land, they retained the Mayflower, the vessel in which they had sailed, as their home. The men went ashore every morning, to work, returning to the little ship, at night. They built a "common house" to which the sick and dying were transferred; placed their four little cannon in a fort, which they built on a hill close by; built two rows of houses, with a wide street between; and lastly landed their stores and provisions. Then the whole company landed, toward the last of March, and in April the Mayflower sailed away.

The winter had been a hard and bitter one. At one time all but six or seven of the Pilgrims were sick; and when spring came, more than half their number had died.

Shortly after the landing of the Pilgrims, while searching for a suitable place in which to build their houses, they one day came upon some deserted Indian huts, in which they found some baskets filled with corn. From this supply they saved enough to plant their first year's crop.

Samoset, who had seen Englishmen along the coast of Maine, and Squanto, who had himself been in England, and the great chief Massasoit, all visited the newcomers and extended a welcome to them. Friendly relations were thus established with the Indians, and a treaty of peace was contracted. The Pilgrims owed much, both at that time, and for years after, to the red men for instructions as to climate, planting of grain and procuring of game.

In the spring of 1621, their seed was sown, and throughout its growing was watched most anxiously. For well they realized that upon this first harvest depended the prosperity of the little colony, and even their lives. To their great joy, the harvest gathered in, in October, was beautiful; and carrying out, no doubt, the idea of the English harvest home, which lasted a week, Governor Bradford ordered a three days' feast and celebration, to which were bidden Chief Massasoit and their other Indian friends.

Wild turkeys, geese, ducks and water fowl, fish, especially cod and shell fish; barley loaves corn bread and vegetables, no doubt formed the chief viands at their feast, not to speak of the five deer, brought in as an offering by the Indians.

By a great many persons, this celebration is believed to be the first Thanksgiving, from which we date our celebration of the day, but well-known writers deny this, one saying: "There is no record of any special religious service during this week of feasting."

But little did the colonists, while feasting

and making merry, think of the hard times
ahead of them. The year 1622 was filled with
misfortune. A short time after the harvest
festival, the ship "Fortune" arrived, but the
only fortune she brought to the Pilgrims was
a number of colonists, for she left with them
no provisions or supplies.

But the first colonists did not mind this, for
they thought their bountiful crop was enough
for all. So Govenor Winslow sent back, when
the "Fortune" returned to England, a glorious account of their prosperity. He was re-
warded by having the "Charity" and the
"Swan" arrive in the summer, crowded with
some very undesirable people, who formed
the Weymouth colony. They brought no supplies, and soon not only ate up the supplies of
their hosts, but caused such an unfriendly feeling among the Indians that the Pilgrims were
afraid to try to add more cultivated land. So
they had to content themselves with obtaining
supplies from the few fishing vessels which
passed and by an occasional trade with the
Indians, but this was not sufficient to feed the
increased colony. The harvest, that fall, did
not yield so well as that of the year before,
and the poor Pilgrims had neither the heart
nor the food for a second week of feasting.

Food became scarcer every day, and the
gloomy winter passed, and each one was glad
to see the spring come. But, although hope

sprang up in their hearts, as the time for planting approached, they were again doomed to bitter disappointment. They finished their planting in April, and hoped that with the harvesting of this crop their hardships would be over.

But the third week in May a drought set in, and the growing crop was withered and almost destroyed. This drought lasted until July, and for relief in their great need, a day was appointed for special fasting and prayer, and after nine hours' prayer, with great joy the Pilgrims saw clouds spread over the sky, from which descended, the next morning, a gentle rain, which revived the corn and brought hope again into the hearts of the colonists.

Captain Miles Standish returned, a few days after this feast, from a little voyage which he had taken, in the hope of procuring provisions. He brought not only food, but the glad news that a ship had been seen bearing in that direction.

The colonists thought it only right, in acknowledgment of all these blesings, to hold a public service of prayer and thanksgiving. On the 30th of July this thanksgiving was held, and the day afterward the "Anne" anchored, containing many of those friends, that for lack of room, the Mayflower had been obliged to leave behind at Leyden.

We may justly claim this feast as the origin of our Thanksgiving Day, not only because, as stated before, it was both a religious and a social celebration, but also because it was the first time in the history of America that the Governor appointed a day for thanksgiving. All former observances of special days had been appointed by the church.

But, like the three days' feast of 1621, this celebration in 1623, although without doubt the origin of our national Thanksgiving Day, may be looked upon as merely a local observance, being held by only the Plymouth colony. They, however, were the forerunners of other more or less local celebrations in Massachusetts, and gradually in other colonies, for in 1630 a public Thanksgiving Day was observed in Boston, by the Bay colony, and again in 1631.

In that year the colonists, who had been comparatively prosperous, met with reverses. Their crop failed, and they were soon reduced to the same want which had befallen the Plymouth colony, nearly ten years before. The women, brave as the men, learned (probably from the Indians, who taught the Pilgrims a great many useful things) how to make a kind of flour from acorns. The children dug clams and mussels; but the ground was hard and frozen, and the few shell-fish they could obtain did not go far toward increasing their supplies; for their stock of corn was now almost used up.

The " Lyon" which lay at the Isle of Shoals, was hired by Governor Winthrop, to go back to England and bring a supply of food, but winter came and the vessel had not yet returned. The increasing cold weather caused a scarcity of game, while the snow hid the acorns and ground nuts, which had become their bread-stuff. The small supply of corn dwindled each day, and it was at this point, as the story goes, that on the verge of starvation, five kernels of corn were appointed to each colonist, as a daily ration.

A fast day was appointed; that is, not a day merely for the abstinence of food, for, in the condition of affairs, that, were unnecessary, but a special day of prayer. To the great joy of the colonists, just at this time, when they were in the greatest need, the " Lyon," filled with provisions, sailed into the harbor. The appointed fast day was turned into one of thanksgiving and rejoicing, and so on February 22nd, 1631, occured in Boston the first Thanksgiving Day of which any written record remains in the Colonial Records of Massachusetts.

The first record of a joint observance was when, in 1632, Governor Winthrop of Massachusetts Bay appointed a day of thanksgiving, and asked the Governor of Plymouth colony to unite in its celebration.

Though in the next fifty years there were as many as twenty-two public thanksgiving days appointed in Massachusetts, usually in October or November, after the gathering in of the harvest, or to celebrate some public benefit, it did not become a regular holiday for a long time afterward. In 1677 the first regular Thanksgiving Proclamation was printed in Massachusetts.

As people of other creeds began to settle in Plymouth colony, over whom the Puritan church had no authority, it was thought necessary to have a law to govern public fasts and thanksgivings, and which should render the day a more general one. Therefore, on November 15th, 1636, this law was framed:

"That it be in the power of the Governor and assistants to command solemn daies of humiliacon by fasting, etc., and also thanksgiving as occasion shall be offered."

So, you see, that even this law only called for an occasional celebration, and not a regular annual observance. After the passage of this law, judging from the data furnished by the church records, which, beside the wording of the law itself, is the only evidence remaining, we find that the civil authority did not take the matter entirely out of the hands of the church, especially in Plymouth colony. They rather combined with the church, for instead of "ordering" the appointment of a certain day, they "proposed" or "desired" the appointment to the churches.

We find that there was no *civil* appointment of a harvest festival in Plymouth colony before 1668, although such a festival had, beyond doubt, become customary in the several communities. But in the Plymouth Records of that year we find the first Thanksgiving proclamation which makes mention of the harvest in these words:

"It hath pleased God in some comfortable measure to bless us in the fruites of the earth."

November 25th was the day appointed.

The form of recommendation in Plymouth colony in 1689 goes to show that it had become an annual custom, and even in 1678 there is good evidence that Plymouth church was observing an annual Thanksgiving Day, usually in the autumn. That year the day appointed was November 6th. The next year, February 25th was the day, and the appointment was made by the church while that of the following year, October 20th, was made by the court.

We find that this system of appointment, one year by the court and another year by the church, prevailed from 1668, and was observed annually, with the exception of some few

years, when for a special cause, as for instance,
during King Philip's War, it was interrupted
for the one year.

· Before 1668, when the church alone exer-
cised the power of appointment, there is no
doubt that in a good many cases, where records of a Thanksgiving celebration cannot be
found, their absence is due to the fact that, on
account of some public misfortune, the day
was kept as a fast day, and one of mourning,
instead of one of rejoicing. And after com-
bining with the civil authorities in the appointment, the church had so much influence
that this peculiar view was still carried out.

The other New England colonies soon followed the lead of Massachusetts in the matter
of keeping Thanksgiving Day. In Connecticut, especially, the church did not care to exercise so much authority, and the appointing
power was early given over entirely to the
government. In this colony, also, the observance of the day was more regular than in Massachusetts Bay or Plymouth colonies, for with
one exception, records are extant for every
year since 1647. This was in 1675, when on
account of Indian massacres, no celebration
was held in Connecticut. Two proclamations
have been found before that date, the earlier,
and no doubt the first proclamation ever issued, in Connecticut, being dated September
18th, 1639.

The cause of this difference between the colonies is, perhaps, owing to the fact that the people of Connecticut were more cheerful than those of their sister colonies, and found many a cause for gratitude, even in years of general misfortune.

Thus, though to the Pilgrims of Plymouth or to the Puritans of Boston, may be traced the origin of Thanksgiving Day, the civil authority and constancy of the people of Connecticut have brought it down to us, not as kept in Massachusetts Bay and Plymouth colony, as an occasional day for a special cause, but as an annual celebration.

In 1644, the first record of a public Dutch Thanksgiving Day is noted, the day being set apart in gratitude for the safe return of the Dutch soldiers, after a battle with the Connecticut Indians. The next year, a treaty of peace with the Indians was celebrated by a public Thanksgiving Day, and again in 1654 the same method was taken to express the gratitude of the residents of the New Netherlands, for a peace established between themselves and England.

Twenty years later, a regular day was set aside, the council sending out the proclamation to the clergymen, whom they asked to announce it, the previous Sunday, to their congregations, that all might be prepared fittingly to celebrate the occasion. There is reason to believe that this celebration was more of a harvest festival than the first ones had been.

In 1864, Dominie Brown of Wyltwyck asked for an established annual Thanksgiving, but there are no records to show that the desire was carried out, though from 1690 to 1710 celebrations were held almost every year, being called thank-days, instead of Thanksgiving days. When New York came under the sway of England, the English governors followed the example of their Dutch predecessors.

The earliest mention of Thanksgiving in the records of Rhode Island Plantation is in 1687. But attempts to celebrate Thanksgiving Day in Rhode Island did not prove very successful. Whether the people were ungrateful or only stubborn, is not known, but it is said that when Governor Andros ordered them to appear, to celebrate certain days, which he set apart as days of thanksgiving, the order was so contemptuously carried out that several persons were arrested for disobedience of the King's ordinances.

During the Revolutionary War, the people and the Continental army observed an annual Thanksgiving Day, by the proclamation of the Continental Congress. After the peace it was discontinued until 1789.

* * *

Washington's Proclamation was occasionally followed by other Presidents.

About the year 1830 the Governor of New
York appointed a day, and other Northern
Governors quickly followed, and in these
States the custom has, since then, been an an-
nual one.

In the South, Thanksgiving Day was prac-
tically unknown until in 1855, when Governor
Johns of Virginia urged in a letter to the State
Legislature, their recognition of the day, that he
might issue a proclamation. He was advised
not to issue it, as most of the citizens regarded
this day as a relic of Puritanic bigotry. His
action, however, aroused public notice, and a
great dispute arose. In 1857 Governor Wise,
successor to Johns, without asking advice, issued a proclamation, and the people throwing
aside their prejudice, celebrated the day with
true Southern hospitality. The next year eight
Southern States, through their Governors'
proclamations, kept the day; but the coming
on of the Civil War soon put an end to its celebration in the South.

The celebration of the day was thus, for several years, although regularly observed, merely a State affair, when the troubles connected
with the Civil War suspended it for a time, as
fast days were more in accord with the general feeling than feast days. But in 1864, President Lincoln issued a proclamation, appointing the fourth Thursday of November, with a
view of having the day kept, thereafter, an-

nually without interruption. The President's
assassination, the next year, almost caused the
suspension of his own rule, but after being
prevailed upon, President Johnson appointed
the last Thursday in November; and since
that time each President has followed his example.

The Governors of the several States, upon
receiving the President's proclamation, issue
their own, naming the same day. Thus we may
say that since 1865, Thanksgiving Day has
been an annual national holiday. It is the only
religious festival celebrated in the United
States by virtue of the authority of the civil
government.

At the present day, Thanksgiving Day ranks
first among holidays in New England. In
the Middle States perhaps the religious ele-
ment of the day is as well observed, but in New
England it is preeminently the family festival.

THE FEAST OF HARVEST

EDMUND CLARENCE STEDMAN

The fair earth smiled and turned herself and
    woke,
  And to the Sun with nuptial greeting said:—
" I had a dream, wherein it seemed men
    broke

A sovran league, and long years fought and
    bled,
Till down my sweet sides ran my children's
    gore,
  And all my beautiful garments were made
    red,
  And all my fertile fields were thicket-
    grown,
Nor could thy dear light reach me through the
    air;
  At last a voice cried, 'Let them strive no
    more!'"
Then music breathed, and lo! from my de-
    spair
    I awake to joy,— yet would not joy alone!

"For, hark! I hear a murmur on the
    meads,—
  Where as of old my children seek my face,—
The low of kine, the peaceful tramp of steeds,
  Blithe shouts of men in many a pastoral
    place,
The noise of tilth through all my goodliest
    land;
  And happy laughter of a dusky race
    Whose brethren lift them from their
    ancient toil,
  Saying: 'The year of jubilee has come;
Gather the gifts of Earth with equal hand;
    Henceforth ye too may share the birthright
    soil,
The corn, the wine, and all the harvest-home.'

"O, my dear lord, my radiant bridegroom,
        look!
    Behold their joy who sorrowed in my
        dreams,—
The sword a share, the spear a pruning-hook;
    Lo, I awake, and turn me toward thy beams
    Upon my fruitful places in full streams!
        Let there be yield for every living thing;
    The land is fallow,— let there be increase
After the darkness of the sterile night;
    Ay, let us twain a festival of Peace
    Prepare, and hither all my nations bring!"

The fair Earth spake: the glad Sun speeded
        forth,
    Hearing her matron words, and backward
        drave
To frozen caves the icy Wind of the North,—
    And bade the South Wind from the tropic
        wave
Bring watery vapors over river and plain,—
    And bade the East Wind cross her path, and
        lave
        The lowlands, emptying there her laden
            mist,—
    And bade the Wind of the West, the best
        wind, blow
After the early and the latter rain,—
        And beamed himself, and oft the sweet
            Earth kissed,
    While her swift servitors sped to and fro.

Forthwith the troop that, at the beck of Earth,
   Foster her children, brought a glorious store
Of viands, food of immemorial worth,
   Her earliest gifts, her tenderest evermore.
First came the Silvery Spirit, whose marshalled
      files
    Climb up the glades in billowy breakers hoar,
      Nodding their crests,— and at his side
        there sped
    The Golden Spirit, whose yellow harvests
      trail
Across the continents and fringe the isles,
    And freight men's argosies where'er they
      sail:
      O, what a wealth of sheaves he there out-
       spread!

Came the dear Spirit whom Earth doth love
      the best,
    Fragrant of clover-bloom and new- mown
      hay,
Beneath whose mantle weary ones find rest,
    On whose green skirts the little children
      play:
She bore the food our patient cattle crave.
    Next, robed in silk, with tassels scattering
      spray,
      Followed the generous Spirit of the
      Maize,—
And many a kindred shape of high renown

Bore in the clustering grape, the fruits that
        wave
    On orchard branches or in garden's blaze,
And those the wind-shook forest hurtles
        down.

Even thus they laid a great and marvellous
        feast,
    And Earth her children summoned joyously,
Throughout that goodliest land wherein had
        ceased
        The vision of battle, and with glad hands
        free
These took their fill, and plenteous measures
        poured,
        Beside, for those who dwelt beyond the sea;
        Praise, like an increase, upward rose to
        Heaven
        For that full harvest,— and the autumnal
        Sun
Stayed long above,— and ever at the board,
        Peace, white-robed angel, held the high
        seat given,
    And War far off withdrew his visage dun.

BALLAD OF THE THANKSGIVING PIL-
GRIM

CLINTON SCOLLARD

The purple hills of Kirkland
    Stood up against the morn,

As o'er the rutty road there strode
  A pilgrim lean and lorn.

The wood-crowned hills of Kirkland,
  They notched the wan blue sky,
As toward that plodding pilgrim came
  A horseman urging by.

" I prithee, weary pilgrim,
  Now whither dost thou roam?"
" I seek a gabled farmstead set
  Amid these hills of home.

" I seek an ancient rooftree set
  Amid these uplands gray."
" God give thee luck," the horseman cried,
    " This frore Thanksgiving day!"

The quiet hills of Kirkland,
  They saw, when broad noon shone
Above the fair Oriska vale,
  This pilgrim toiling on.

The frosted asters waved and tossed
  Before him and behind;
The journeying silken milkweed seed
  Went capering down the wind.

The hemlocks preened their night-dark plumes
  As up and up he clomb;
The same old rook-calls welcomed him
  Back to the hills of home.

High on the hills of Kirkland
    Where hale the North-wind roared,
O gay were they that grouped about
    The heaped Thanksgiving board!

And yet the brooding mother,
    She hid with smiles the tear
For one whose lips she had not kissed
    This many a lonely year.

For one whose wander-lust had led
    His roving spirit far,
Until she dreamed he slept beneath
    The clear Alaskan star.

Hark, at the door a summons!
    A step upon the sill!
O mother-eyes abrim with joy,
    And mother-heart athrill!

And O ye hills of Kirkland,
    In dull November gray,
Ye never saw a gladder sight
    Upon Thanksgiving day!

THE FIRST THANKSGIVING DAY

KATE DOUGLAS WIGGIN and NORA A. SMITH

Nearly three hundred years ago, a great many of the people in England were very unhappy because their king would not let them pray to God as they liked. The king said they must use the same prayers that he did; and if they would not do this, they were often thrown into prison, or perhaps driven away from home.

"Let us go away from this country," said the unhappy Englishmen to each other; and so they left their homes, and went far off to a country called Holland. It was about this time that they began to call themselves "Pilgrims." Pilgrims, you know, are people who are always traveling to find something they love, or to find a land where they can be happier; and these English men and women were journeying, they said, "from place to place, toward heaven, their dearest country."

In Holland, the Pilgrims were quiet and happy for a while, but they were very poor; and when the children began to grow up, they were not like English children, but talked Dutch, like the little ones of Holland, and

21

some grew naughty and did not want to go to church any more.

"This will never do," said the Pilgrim fathers and mothers; so after much talking and thinking and writing they made up their minds to come here to America. They hired two vessels, called the Mayflower and the Speedwell, to take them acros the sea; but the Speedwell was not a strong ship, and the captain had to take her home again before she had gone very far.

The Mayflower went back, too. Part of the Speedwell's passengers were given to her, and then she started alone across the great ocean.

There were one hundred people on board,—mothers and fathers, brothers and sisters and little children. They were very crowded; it was cold and uncomfortable; the sea was rough, and pitched the Mayflower about, and they were two months sailing over the water.

The children cried many times on the journey, and wished they had never come on the tiresome ship that rocked them so hard, and would not let them keep still a minute.

But they had one pretty plaything to amuse them, for in the middle of the great ocean a Pilgrim baby was born, and they called him "Oceanus," for his birthplace. When the children grew so tired that they were cross and fretful, Oceanus' mother let them come and play with him, and that always brought smiles and happy faces back again.

At last the Mayflower came in sight of land; but if the children had been thinking of grass and flowers and birds, they must have been very much disappointed, for the month was cold November, and there was nothing to be seen but rocks and sand and hard bare ground.

Some of the Pilgrim fathers, with brave Captain Miles Standish at their head, went on shore to see if they could find any houses or white people. But they only saw some wild Indians, who ran away from them, and found some Indian huts, and some corn buried in holes in the ground. They went to and fro from the ship three times, till by and by they found a pretty place to live, where there were "fields and little running brooks."

Then at last all the tired Pilgrims landed from the ship on a spot now called Plymouth Rock, and the first house was begun on Christmas Day. But when I tell you how sick they were and how much they suffered that first winter, you will be very sad and sorry for them. The weather was cold, the snow fell fast and thick, the wind was icy, and the Pilgrim fathers had no one to help them cut down the trees and build their church and their houses.

The Pilgrim mothers helped all they could; but they were tired with the long journey, and cold, and hungry too, for no one had the right kind of food to eat, nor even enough of it.

So first one was taken sick, and then another,

till half of them were in bed at the same time.
Brave Miles Standish and the other soldiers
nursed them as well as they knew how; but before spring came half of the people died and
had gone at last to " heaven, their dearest country."

But by and by the sun shone more brightly,
the snow melted, the leaves began to grow, and
sweet spring had come again.

Some friendly Indians had visited the Pilgrims during the winter, and Captain Miles
Standish, with several of his men, had returned
the visit.

One of the kind Indians was called Squanto,
and he came to stay with the Pilgrims, and
showed them how to plant their corn, and their
peas and wheat and barley.

When the summer came and the days were
long and bright, the Pilgrim children were
very happy, and they thought Plymouth a
lovely place indeed. All kinds of beautiful
wild flowers grew at their doors, there were
hundreds of birds and butterflies, and the great
pine woods were always cool and shady when
the sun was too bright.

When it was autumn the fathers gathered
the barley and wheat and corn that they had
planted, and found that it had grown so well
that they would have quite enough for the long
winter that was coming.

" Let us thank God for it all," they said.

" It is He who has made the sun shine and the rain fall and the corn grow." So they thanked God in their homes and in their little church; the fathers and the mothers and the children thanked Him.

" Then," said the Pilgrim mothers, " let us have a great Thanksgiving party, and invite the friendly Indians, and all rejoice together."

So they had the first Thanksgiving party, and a grand one it was! Four men went out shooting one whole day, and brought back so many wild ducks and geese and great wild turkeys that there was enough for almost a week. There was deer meat also, of course, for there were plenty of fine deer in the forest. Then the Pilgrim mothers made the corn and wheat into bread and cakes, and they had fish and clams from the sea besides.

The friendly Indians all came with their chief Massasoit. Every one came that was invited, and more, I dare say, for there were ninety of them altogether.

They brought five deer with them, that they gave to the Pilgrims; and they must have liked the party very much, for they stayed three days.

Kind as the Indians were, you would have been very much frightened if you had seen them; and the baby Oceanus, who was a year old then, began to cry at first whenever they came near him.

They were dressed in deerskins, and some of them had the furry coat of a wild cat hanging on their arms. Their long black hair fell loose on their shoulders, and was trimmed with feathers or fox-tails. They had their faces painted in all kinds of strange ways, some with black stripes as broad as your finger all up and down them. But whatever they wore, it was their very best, and they had put it on for the Thanksgiving party.

Each meal, before they ate anything, the Pilgrims and the Indians thanked God together for all his goodness. The Indians sang and danced in the evenings, and every day they ran races and played all kinds of games with the children.

Then sometimes the Pilgrims with their guns, and the Indians with their bows and arrows, would see who could shoot farthest and best. So they were glad and merry and thankful for three whole days.

The Pilgrim mothers and fathers had been sick and sad many times since they landed from the Mayflower; they had worked very hard, often had not had enough to eat, and were mournful indeed when their friends died and left them. But now they tried to forget all this, and think only of how good God had been to them; and so they all were happy together at the first Thanksgiving party.

* * * * * * * * * * *

All this happened nearly three hundred years ago, and ever since that time Thanksgiving has been kept in our country.

Every year our fathers and grandfathers and great-grandfathers have " rejoiced together " like the Pilgrims, and have had something to be thankful for each time.

Every year some father has told the story of the brave Pilgrims to his little sons and daughters, and has taught them to be very glad and proud that the Mayflower came sailing to our country so many years ago.

THE FIRST THANKSGIVING DAY

ALICE WILLIAMS BROTHERTON

In Puritan New England a year had passed
    away
Since first beside the Plymouth coast the Eng-
    lish Mayflower lay,
When Bradford, the good Governor, sent fowl-
    ers forth to snare
The turkey and the wild-fowl, to increase the
    scanty-fare :—

" Our husbandry hath prospered, there is corn
    enough for food,
Though ' the pease be parched in blossom, and
    the grain indifferent good.'

Who blessed the loaves and fishes for the feast
  miraculous,
And filled with oil the widow's cruse, He hath
  remembered us!

" Give thanks unto the Lord of Hosts, by whom
  we all are fed,
Who granted us our daily prayer, ' Give us our
  daily bread!'
By us and by our children let this day be kept
  for aye,
In memory of His bounty, as the land's Thanksgiving Day."

Each brought his share of Indian meal the
  pious feast to make,
With the fat deer from the forest and the wild-
  fowl from the brake.
And chanted hymn and prayer were raised —
  though eyes with tears were dim —
" The Lord He hath remembered us, let us remember Him!"

Then Bradford stood up at their head and lifted
  up his voice:
" The corn is gathered from the field, I call you
  to rejoice;
Thank God for all His mercies, from the greatest to the least,
Together have we *fasted,* friends, together let
  us *feast.*

" The Lord who led forth Israel was with us in
   the waste :
Sometime in light, sometime in cloud, before us
   He hath paced ;
Now give Him thanks, and pray to Him who
   holds us in His hand
To prosper us and make of this a strong and
   mighty land ! "

*   *   *   *   *   *   *   *

From Plymouth to the Golden Gate to-day
   their children tread,
The mercies of that bounteous Hand upon the
   land are shed ;
The " flocks are on a thousand hills," the prai-
   ries wave with grain,
The cities spring like mushrooms now where
   once was desert-plain.

Heap high the board with plenteous cheer and
   gather to the feast,
And toast that sturdy Pilgrim band whose
   courage never ceased.
Give praise to that All-Gracious One by whom
   their steps were led,
And thanks unto the harvest's Lord who sends
   our " daily bread."

GRANDMA'S THANKSGIVING STORY

ALICE LOTHERINGTON

It was getting toward bedtime in the house on the hill, and the children had gathered about the fire, for a talk with grandma before going to bed.

"Listen," said Willie, "how the wind blows down the chimney. I think Jack Frost must be out to-night." Just then Jane came in to put coal on the fire, and told the little folks it was snowing. "Hurrah!" cried Joey, "we'll have snow for Thanksgiving. Won't that be jolly?"

"Boys," said sister Nettie, as she looked at the clock, "only twenty minutes more before bedtime; if we don't look out it will be too late for grandma's story, and you know we don't want to miss that."

"Indeed we don't," said the boys, and they drew their chairs closer, while little Bess nestled in grandma's lap.

"What shall the story be about, dears?" asked grandma.

"A Thanksgiving story, please," answered Joey, "a *really* and *truly* one."

"I'll tell you about a Thanksgiving long, long ago," said grandma, after a minute's thought. "Were there any little boys and girls in the story?" asked Bess. Grandma nodded.

"Once upon a time, many years ago, there were a number of people who lived in a country called England. These people, Puritans they were called, were not happy in their old home, so they thought that they would come over the big ocean and make another home for themselves, in the new world, which a man named Christopher Columbus had discovered a long time before. The name of the new country was America. Now these people had two ships named 'Speedwell' and 'Mayflower,' in which they were to sail across the ocean to their new home.

"Just as they were about to start, it was found that the 'Speedwell' was not fit to go so far, so all the people had to go in the 'Mayflower.'

"One beautiful morning in September, after bidding their friends good-by, the little band set sail in the 'Mayflower.'

"For four long months they were upon the ocean, but at last they landed on the shore of Massachusetts, in December, 1620.

"It was bitter cold, so the men left the women and children on the ship while they

went on land to build log houses for their
families to live in.

"When springtime came the people planted
corn; but they planted too soon, and Jack Frost
came, pinched the tiny shoots just coming out
of the ground, and the corn died.

"Still our friends kept cheerful and made
the best of what they had, for they knew there
was a big ship coming from England with more
corn and good things on board.

"But the ship did not come, and the store of
food got less and less.

"How the people watched for that ship!
Little children would go down to the shore,
shade their eyes with their hands and look far
over the water, to see if the ship was coming.

"One morning some one spied a white sail
in the distance, which grew larger and larger,
and at last came to anchor in their harbor.
How happy the people were, for it was the
ship which they had been looking for so long.
There would be plenty to eat now.

"The Governor had the church bell rung,
and all the people, big and little, gathered together and gave thanks to God for sending
food to them.

"You may be sure that there were good
dinners cooked that day, and all the boys and
girls had as much as they could eat.

"When the next spring came, the people

were careful not to plant the corn too soon, so Jack Frost could not hurt it, and in the fall they reaped a good harvest, and had plenty of corn for the next winter."

" Is that a really and truly story, grandma? " asked Bess.

" Yes, dear," answered grandma.

" Is that the reason we keep Thanksgiving to-morow? " said Joey.

" Not exactly," replied grandma; " the President of the United States tells the people to have a Thanksgiving on the last Thursday in November, to thank God for the harvest, and all the blessings He has given to us for the past year.

" But, little folks, the clock is going to strike nine, so give grandma a kiss and away to bed, and dream of the good time you will have to-morrow with your cousins, for you know they are coming to spend Thanksgiving with you."

THE FIRST THANKSGIVING

BOSTON, 1631

ARTHUR GUITERMAN

The curse of Cain was on the earth;
　　The leaden heavens frowned;
The winter closed with cruel dearth
　　And gripped the fruitless ground.

Behind us rose the sombre wood,
    Before us stretched the foam —
A thousand leagues of briny flood
    That sundered us from home.

The meagre mussel was our meat;
    We robbed the squirrels' hoard;
Our barren glebe beneath our feet,
    We cried upon the Lord.

"Arouse your souls against despair,"
    The godly Winthrop said,
"And choose a day of fast and prayer,
    For, surely, He who led

Our wanderings across the wave
    Shall hear us when we plead.
And stretch a mighty arm to save
    His people in their need."

Behold! When all is black and drear
    And want assails the land,
How God delighteth to appear
    To work with wond'rous hand!

For, even as we made to deal
    To one that hungered sore,
The utmost handful of our meal,
    A shout arose from shore.

An hundred watching eyes descried
    Through winter's misty pall,

The good ship Lion breast the tide
   With provender for all.

Then joined the voice of first and least
   A hymn of thanks to raise,
Our day of fasting changed to feast
   And prayer gave way to praise

So once in every year we throng
   Upon a day apart,
To praise the Lord with feast and song
   In thankfulness of heart.

———

THE FIRST THANKSGIVING DAY OF NEW ENGLAND

FROM STANDISH OF STANDISH

JANE G. AUSTIN

" Oh Priscilla, girl, what thinkest thou is toward now," demanded Mary Chilton, running down to the spring where her friend was sprinkling and turning a piece of coarse linen spun and woven by her own hands for domestic use; but straightening herself at the merry summons, her dark eyes lighted with animation as she responded in the same tone,—

" The governor is fain to marry thee, and the elder is ready to give his blessing. Is't so."

" Thou foolish girl! It's not at me Master Bradford looks oftenest, not nigh as often as the captain looks at thee, nay but John Alden —"

" What is it! What's thy news! Speak quick or I'll sprinkle thee rather than the linen!" and raising the wooden dipper Priscilla whirled it so rapidly round her head that not a drop was spilled, while Mary shrieking and laughing darted back and crouched behind an alder bush.

"Maids! Maids! Whence this unseemly mirth! Know ye not that the laughter of fools is like the crackling of thorns under the pot, a sure sign of the fire they are hastening to? The devil goeth about like a roaring lion —"

"Sometimes methinks he seemeth more like an ass," murmured Priscilla in Mary's ear, setting her off into convulsions of repressed laughter, while her naughty tormentor looked demurely up the bank to the angular figure defined against the evening sky and said,—

"We are beholden to you for the admonition, Master Allerton, and it must be a marvelous comfort to you that Mary and Remember Allerton weep so much oftener than they laugh."

"I would, thou froward wench, that I had the training of thee for a while. Mayhap thou wouldst find cause for weeping —"

"Nay, I'm sure on 't. The very thought well-nigh makes me weep now," retorted Priscilla blithely, as the sour visaged Councilor went on his way, and Mary half frightened, half delighted, came forward saying,—

"Oh Priscilla, how dost thou dare flout Master Allerton in that style! He'll have thee before the Church."

"Not he!" replied Priscilla coolly. "Hist now, poppet, and I'll tell thee something — thoul't not repeat it though?"

"Not I," replied Mary stoutly.

"Well, then, dost think I should make a fitting stepdame for Bartholomew and Mary and Remember?"

"Dost mean —"

"Ay do I, just that. And because I could not but laugh merrily at the notion when 'twas placed before me last Sunday night, the Assistant looketh sourly enough but dareth not meddle with me lest I make others laugh as well as myself."

"Priscilla! Mary!" called Elizabeth Tilley's voice from the doorstep. "Mistress Brewster would have you in to see about noon-meat."

"But thy news, poppet, quick!" exclaimed Priscilla as gathering up her gear she slowly led the way up the hill.

"Why, the governor hath resolved upon a day, or rather a week, of holiday and of thanksgiving for the mercies God hath showed us. Think of it, Pris! A whole week of feasting and holiday!"

"Hm!" dryly responded Priscilla. "It sounds well enow, but who is to make ready this feasting?"

"Why — all of us — and chiefly you, dear wench, for none can season a delicate dish or —"

"Ay, ay, I know that song full well; but dost really think, Molly, that to do a good deal more, and a good deal harder cooking than our wont, will be so very sprightly a holiday?"

"But 'twill be doing our part to make holiday for the others," replied Mary simply.

"Now, then, if thou'rt not at thy old tricks of shaming my selfish frowardness!" exclaimed Priscilla, and laughing they entered the house where all the women of the community were assembled in eager debate over their share in the approaching festival.

"The governor hath already ordered my man, with Dotey and Soule and Latham, to go afield to-morrow with their guns, and to spend two days in gathering game," announced Helen Billington with an air of importance.

"And it was determined to invite King Massasoit and his train to the feast," eagerly added Mistress Winslow, who, with her baby Peregrine White in her arms, had run across the street to join the council.

"Methinks another party should go to the beach to dig clams," suggested Dame Hopkins. "For though not so toothsome as venison and birds 'tis a prey more surely to be come by."

"The elder saith the God of Jacob sendeth us the clams as he did manna to those other children of his in the desert," added the weak, sweet voice of the elder's wife. "At morning and at night we may gather them in certainty."

"But they hold not sweet over Sunday, that

is if the day be hot," suggested Desire Minter
ruefully.

"And Priscilla we shall look to thee for
marchpanes and manchets and plum-porridge
and possets and all-manner of tasty eates, such
as only thou canst make," said the dame hastily, and fixing her eyes upon the girl's face as
if to hinder any irreverent laughter at Desire's
speech.

"All that I can do I will do blithely and
steadfastly if it will pleasure you, mother,"
replied Priscilla gently, as she knelt down beside the invalid and rested against the arm of
that old chair which you may see to-day reverently preserved in Plymouth.

"I know thou wilt, sweetheart," replied the
dame laying her frail hand upon the girl's
abundant hair. "But I fear me our men cannot dine to-day on the promise of the coming
feast."

"Well thought on, mother. Come, maids, to
work, to work!"

That same afternoon Squanto was dispatched
to Namasket to send from thence a runner to
Massasoit inviting him, with his brother and a
fitting escort, to the feast of Thanksgiving now
fixed for the following Thursday; and so cor-
dially did the great sachem respond, that about
sunrise on the appointed day the laggards of
the settlement were aroused by the terrific

whoop and succession of unearthly shrieks with which the guests announced at once their arrival and their festive and playful condition of mind.

Three of the leaders were ready even at this hour to receive the over punctual guests; the elder, who had risen early to prepare a few brief remarks suited to the occasion; Standish, who was always afoot to fire his sunrise gun; and Bradford, who valued the quiet morning hour in which he might allow his mind to dwell upon those abstruse and profound subjects so dear to his heart, and yet never allowed to intrude upon the business of the working day. So, while Winslow with his wife's assistance did on his more festive doublet and hose, and Allison spake bitter words to Remember who had forgotten to replace the button that should hold her father's collar in place, and gentle Warren, the gruff Surgeon, and the rest made ready as they might, these three stood forth to receive Massasoit and Quadequina, who with a dozen or so of their principal Pnieses came forward with considerable dignity, and through Squanto and Hobomok made their compliments in truly regal style, while their followers to the number of about ninety men with a few women remained modestly in the background.

Presently when the village was well afoot, and a big fire started between the elder's house

and the brook for cooking purposes, the roll
of the drum announced the morning prayers,
with which the Pilgrims began every day, and
more especially this Feast of Thanksgiving.
The Indians stood reverently around, Massasoit explaining in low gutturals to a chieftain
who had never visited Plymouth before, that
the white men thus propitiated the Great Spirit,
and engaged Him both to prosper them and kill
their enemies.

Prayers ended, Priscilla with her attendants
flew back to the fire, and presently a long table
spread in the open air for the men was covered
with great wooden bowls full of what a later
generation named hasty-pudding, to be eaten
with butter and treacle, for milk was not to be
had for more than one year to come. Other
bowls contained an excellent clam chowder
with plenty of sea biscuit swimming in the
savory broth, while great pieces of cold boiled
beef with mustard, flanked by dishes of turnips, offered solid resistance to those who so
joyfully attacked them.

Another table in the Common house offered
somewhat more delicate food to the women and
children, chief among it a great pewter bowl
of plum-porridge with bits of toasted cracker
floating upon it.

The meal was a rude one looked upon with
the dainty eyes and languid appetites of to-
day, but to those sturdy and heroic men and

women it was a veritable feast, and at its close Quadequina with an amiable smile nodded to one of his attendants, who produced and poured upon the table something like a bushel of popped corn,— a dainty, hitherto unseen and unknown by most of the Pilgrims.

All tasted, and John Howland hastily gathering up a portion upon a wooden plate carried it to the Common house for the delectation of the women, that is to say, for Elizabeth Tilley, whose firm young teeth crunched it with much gusto.

Breakfast over, with a grace after meat that amounted to another service, the governor announced that some military exercises under the direction of Captain Standish would now take place, and the guests were invited to seat them-selves in the vicinity of a fire kindled on the ground at the northerly part of the village about at the head of Middle Street, and designed more as a common centre and social feature than for need since the weather was mild and lovely, so peculiarly so that when it recurred the next November and the next, the people remembering that first feast said, " Why here is the Indians' summer again ! " But on that day the only thought was that God accepted their thanksgiving and smiled His approval.

Hardly had the guests comprehended the announcement and placed themselves in order, when a wild fanfare of trumpets, an imposing roll of drums was heard from the vicinity of the Fort, and down the hill in orderly array marched the little army of nineteen men, preceded by the military band and led by their doughty Captain. Above their heads floated the banner of Old England, and beneath their corselets beat true English hearts; and yet here stood the nucleus of that power which a century and a half later was to successfully defy and throw off the rule of that magnificent but cruel stepdame; here stood the first American army; and then, as since, that score of determined souls struck terror into the hearts of five times their number.

"If they have beguiled us here to destroy us!" murmured Quadequina in his brother's ear.

"Canst not tell an eagle from a carrion-crow?" returned the wiser man. "Would Winslow, or The-Sword, or the Chief, or the powah, do this? Peace, my brother."

But as the military manœuvres accompanied with frequent discharges of musketry, and accented at one point with a tremendous roar from the cannon of the Fort progressed, not only Quadequina, but many others of the braves became very uneasy; and to this cause as well as benevolence, may be attributed the offer made at dinner time by Quadequina to lead a hunting party of his own people into the woods to look for deer, whose haunts they well knew.

Standish alone suspected this *arrière pensée,*
and when Bradford mildly applauded the generous kindness of their guests, he answered
with a chuckle,—

" Ay, as kind as the traveler who begs the
highwayman to let him go home and fetch a
larger treasure."

But in spite of his doubts the prince intended
and made a *bonâ fide* hunt, and returned early
in the next day with as much venison as lasted
the entire company four days.

" Oh, if I had but some Spanish chestnuts to
stuff these turkeys, they might seem more like
their brethren across the sea," exclaimed Priscilla as she turned over a pile of the wild birds
and chose those to be first cooked.

" Nay, but to me the flavor is better, and the
meat more succulent of these than of any I
ever saw at home," replied John Alden. " And
the size! Do but look at this fellow, he will
scale well-nigh twenty pound if an ounce."

" If 'twere a goose I would name it John,
'twould be so prodigious a goose," replied Priscilla with a glance so saucy and so bewitching
that her adorer forgot to reply, and she went
briskly on,—

" Come now, young man, there's much to do
and scant time to talk of it. Call me some of
those gaping boys yonder and let them pluck
these fowls, and bid John Billington come and
break up these deer. And I must have wood

and water galore to make meat for a hundred men. Stir thyself!"

" I was thinking, Priscilla — why not stuff the turkeys with beechnuts? There is store of them up at our cottage."

" How came they there? Doth our doughty Captain go birdsnesting and nutting in his by-times?"

" Nay, but I did, that is, I gathered the nuts for thee, and then — then feared if I offered them thou'dst only flout me —"

" Oh, sure never was a poor maid so bestead with blind men — well, fetch thy beechnuts."

" Nay, Priscilla, but blind, blind? How then am I blind, maiden, say?"

" Why, not to have discovered ere this how I dote upon beechnuts. There, get thee gone for them."

The dressing of beechnuts proved a rare success, but the preparation proved so long a process that only the delicate young bird made ready for the table where Mistress Brewster presided was thus honored, although in after times Priscilla often made what she called goose-dressing; and when a few years later some sweet potatoes were brought to Plymouth from the Carolinas, she at once adopted them for the same purpose.

And so the festival went on for its appointed length of three days, and perhaps the hearty fellowship and good will manifested by the white men toward their guests, and their determination to meet them on the ground of common interests and sympathies, went quite as far as their evident superiority in arms and resources toward establishing the deep-founded and highly valued peace, without which the handful of white men could never have made good their footing upon that stern and sterile coast.

On the Saturday the feast was closed by a state dinner whose composition taxed Priscilla as head cook to the limit of her resources, and with flushed cheek and knitted brow she moved about among her willing assistants with all the importance of a Bechamel, a Felix, the *maitre-d'hôtel of* Cardinal Fesch with his two turbots, or luckless Vatel who fell upon his sword and died because he had no turbot at all; or even, rising in the grandeur of the comparison, we may liken her to Domitian, who weary of persecuting Christians, one day called the Roman Senate together to decide with him upon the sauce with which another historic turbot should be dressed.

Some late arrivals among the Indians had that morning brought in several large baskets of the delicious oysters for which Wareham is still famous, and although it was an unfamiliar delicacy to her, Priscilla, remembering a tradition brought from Ostend to Leyden by some travelers, compounded these with biscuit-crumbs, spices, and wine, and was looking about for an iron pan wherein to bake them, when Elizabeth Tilley brought forward some great clam and scallop shells which John Howland had presented to her, just as now a young man might offer a unique Sèvres tea-set to the lady of his love.

"Wouldn't it do to fill these with thy oyster compote, and so set them in the ashes to roast?" inquired she. "Being many they can be laid at every man's place at table."

"Why, 'tis a noble idea, child," exclaimed Priscilla eagerly. "'Twill be a novelty, and will set off the board famously. Say you not so, John?"

"Ay," returned Alden, who was busily opening the oysters at her side. "And more by token there is a magnificence in the idea that thou hast not thought on; for as at a great man's table the silver dishes each bear the crest of his arms, so we being Pilgrims and thus privileged to wear the scallop shell in our hats, do rather choose to display it upon our board."

"Ah, John, thou hast an excellent wit — in *some* things," replied Priscilla with a half sigh which set the young fellow wondering for an hour.

By noon the long tables were spread, and still the sweet warm air of the "Indian Summer" made the out-of-door feast not only possible but charming, for the gauzy veil upon the distant forest, and the marine horizon, and the curves of Captain's Hill, seemed to shut in this little scene from all the world of turmoil and danger and fatigue, while the thick yellow sunshine filtered through with just warmth enough for comfort, and the sighing southerly breeze brought wafts of perfume from the forest, and bore away, as it wandered northward, the peals of laughter, the merry yet discreet songs, and the multitudinous hum of blithe voices, Saxon and savage, male and female, adult and childish, that filled the dreamy air.

The oysters in their scallop shells were a singular success, and so were the mighty venison pasties, and the savory stew compounded of all that flies the air, and all that flies the hunter in Plymouth woods, no longer flying now but swimming in a glorious broth cunningly seasoned by Priscilla's anxious hand, and thick bestead with dumplings of barley flour, light, toothsome, and satisfying. Beside these were roasts of various kinds, and thin cakes of bread or manchets, and bowls of salad set off with wreaths of autumn leaves laid around them, and great baskets of grapes, white and purple, and of the native plum, so delicious when fully ripe in its three colors of black, white, and red. With these were plentiful flagons of ale, for already the housewives had laid down the first brewing of the native brand, and had moreover learned of the In-

dians to concoct a beverage akin to what is now
called root beer, well flavored with sassafras,
of which the Pilgrims had been glad to find
good store since it brought a great price in the
English market.

It was during the last half hour of this feast
that Desire Minter, who with the other girls
served the tables where the men sat at meat,
placed a little silver cup at Captain Standish's
right hand saying,—

"Priscilla sends you some shrub, kind sir,
of her own composition, and prays you drink
her health."

"Why, then, 'tis kind of her who hath been
most unkind of late," returned Miles, upon
whose seasoned brain the constant potations of
three days had wrought to lull suspicion and
reserve, and taking the cup he tossed off its
contents at a draught, and rising bowed toward
Priscilla who was flitting in and out among
the tables. She returned the salute with a
little air of surprise, and Miles reseating himself turned to question Desire again, but she
had departed carrying the cup with her.

"Nay, then, I'll be toyed with no longer,"
muttered the Captain angrily, and although he
bore his part in the closing ceremonies with
which the governor bade a cordial and even
affectionate farewell to the king, the prince,
their nobles, and their following, there was a
glint in his eye and a set to his lips that would

have told one who knew him well that the spirit of the man was roused and not lightly to be laid to rest again.

FESTIVAL DAYS

HARRY CASSELL DAVIS, A.M., PH. D.

November has one day which is sacred in the family calendar. It is a day of memories and renewals of fellowships and family goodwill. It is a day to which allusion was made in Mosaic times, in the words of Leviticus: " Then shall he offer with the sacrifice of thanksgiving," and it is again adumbrated in the words of the angels: " Blessings and glory and wisdom and thanksgiving and honor and power and might be unto our God forever and ever." All the way through this chapter of Old Testament times there is frequent mention of such a state of mind and heart as might reasonably result in a gladsome thanksgiving Day, when the Pilgrims reached the New World and when Puritan rigidity melted in the glow of Puritan faith.

The observance of Thanksgiving Day has been common in New England ever since the days of the Mayflower, when the self-exiled band of devoted Christians reached the shores of Cape Cod, where they rejoiced in the goodness which had preserved them while they crossed the ocean in search of religious freedom. How often our hearts have thrilled as we have sung or heard others sing of the far-off Pilgrim days, when the heroic men and women of that pioneer company lifted their hearts and voices in thanksgiving and praise.

" Amidst the storm they sang,
　And the stars heard and the sea,
'And the sounding aisles of the dim woods rang
　With the anthem of the free."

Their reasons for thanksgiving have remained to this day, and to them have been added many others. For two centuries, perhaps, this day was observed mainly in New England. Governors there issued yearly proclamations — that of the Pilgrims' own state always with the words: " God save the Commonwealth of Massachusetts!" But after the civil war had knit so many hearts all over the land in defence of " the dear old flag," and especially when peace had come to unify the states, Thanksgiving Day became a general day of praise, with proclamation by the President and everywhere a legal holiday.

In many states it is observed with religious services. In all there is much thankfulness displayed by enjoyment of the bounties of harvest time and by a generous sharing of the good things of life with those less favored. The feathered token of Thanksgiving Day finds its way from employer to employé, and tables laden with edibles brighten the poor man's home and make the day one of the pleasantest of the year, while the rich man learns that ' it is more blessed to give than to receive.' The hearts of both are better qualified for the praises that belong to the brightest of the November days. Bryant wrote of this month as if it were a sombre one. He immortalized the phrase, " The melancholy days " in his couplet:

" The melancholy days are come, the saddest of
the year,
Of wailing winds and naked woods and meadows brown and sere."

But who thinks of dreariness when the family gathering on Thanksgiving Day is a foretaste of that blessed time when the families of earth shall gather in the heavenly home to keep the long and glad and bright Thanksgiving Day of eternity!

———

TWO NOTABLE THANKSGIVINGS

The Youth's Companion

The most joyous Thanksgiving recorded in American annals occurred in May, 1778, when the news arrived that France had concluded a treaty of friendship and alliance with the thirteen States of the American Union. It followed the winter of want and harrowing anxiety which General Washington and his army passed at Valley Forge, on the banks of the Schuylkill, twenty miles above Philadelphia.

Five months before, there had been a Thanksgiving which was far indeed from being a festival in Washington's camp.

Philadelphia had fallen into the hands of the enemy, and when winter approached the American general knew not what to do with his shivering troops. There was no room for them in the country towns of Pennsylvania, which were filled to overflowing with refugees from the captured capital. General Washington, after much reflection, made up his mind to remain where he was and to create a little town of his own for the troops.

So, in his Thanksgiving Proclamation of December 17, 1777, he announced his intention, saying that, "With activity and diligence, huts may be erected that will be warm and dry," in which the troops "will be more secure against surprises and at hand to protect the country." But, first of all, the army must comply with the call of the Honorable Congress to render thanks for the brilliant successes of the recent campaign, which had resulted in the surrender of Burgoyne and his army.

" The general directs that the army remain in its present quarters, and that the chaplains perform divine service with their several corps and brigades, and earnestly exhorts all officers and soldiers, whose absence is not indispensably necessary, to attend with reverence the solemnities of the day."

All of which was punctually observed by the army on the 18th of December.

On the day following the building of log cabins began, a work as familiar to the men of that day as was plowing the fields or swinging the scythe. All the available tools were brought together, and then fairly distributed. The army was divided into parties of twelve, and all set at work building huts designed to lodge that number of men, so that every soldier had the feeling that he was building his own winter home.

General Washington promised to present twelve dollars as a reward to the party in each regiment which should finish its house in the shortest time and in the best manner. He also offered a reward of a hundred dollars to the officer or soldier who, in the scarcity of boards, should invent the best kind of available roofing for the cabins.

Each cabin was to be fourteen feet by sixteen, with a good chimney and fireplace, and all were to be conveniently arranged in streets. The commanding general himself occupied a log cabin during the winter, as he had publicly promised the troops that he would "himself share in the hardships, and partake of every inconvenience."

But then came the starving time! The country around about was supporting two armies, in addition to its ordinary population, and the States were backward in sending supplies. At one time a part of the army went without meat of any kind for a week; those who were most favored were without it for three or four days, and the whole army was so short of clothing that large numbers of the men had not enough covering for decency, to say nothing of comfort.

There was a time in January, 1778, when the surgeons reported three thousand and nineteen men on the sick list, out of a total nominal force of eleven thousand. The British at Philadelphia, twenty miles away, were living in luxury.

Washington never exhibited his eminent qualities in a more striking light than he did during

the winter at Valley Forge. He was then
wholly the great man. The patient endurance
of the men was due in great part to his presence,
to his manifest sympathy with them and his
known activity on their behalf. The measures
which ended the famine, and brought in abundant supplies of clothing and food, were directly
due to his foresight and energy.

Later in the winter when the men had recov-
ered their health and spirits he sent for Mrs.
Washington, and then for the first time he allowed himself the luxury of an extra cabin for
his dining-room. Mrs. Washington herself reports that the cabin in which they slept was very
small and that things were greatly mended when
the new room was added. At last, the great and
glorious news announcing that the infant repub-
lic had found a powerful friend in Europe
reached the camp, reached Congress, and filled
the whole land with joy. General Washington
received the news about the second of May, and
on the sixth he published the following proclamation:

" It having pleased the Almighty Ruler of the
Universe to defend the cause of the United
American States, and finally to raise us up a
powerful friend among the princes of the earth,
to establish our liberty and independency upon
a lasting foundation, it becomes us to set apart a
day for gratefully acknowledging the Divine
Goodness, and celebrating the important event

which we owe to his Divine Interposition. The
several brigades are to be assembled for this
purpose at nine o'clock to-morrow morning,
when their chaplains will communicate the intel-
ligence contained in the postscript of the Pennsylvania Gazette of the second instant, and offer
up thanksgiving, and deliver a discourse suitable
to the occasion.

" At half-past ten o'clock a cannon will be
fired, which is to be a signal for the men to be
under arms; the brigade inspectors will then in-
spect their dress and arms, and form the battalions according to the instructions given them,
and announce to the commanding officers of the
brigade that the battalions are formed.

" The commanders of brigades will then appoint field-officers to the battalions, after which
each battalion will be ordered to hold and
ground their arms. At half-past eleven a second cannon will be fired as a signal for the
march, upon which the several brigades will begin march by wheeling to the right of platoons,
and proceed by the nearest way to the left of
their ground by the new position; this will be
pointed out by the brigade inspectors.

" A third signal will then be given, on which
there will be a discharge of thirteen cannon,
after which a running fire of the infantry will
begin on the right of Woodford's, and will con-
tinue throughout the front line; it will then be
taken up on the left of the second line, and con-

tinue to the right. Upon a signal given, the
whole army will huzza:

"'Long live the King of France!'

"The artillery then begins, and fires thirteen
rounds; this will be succeeded by a second general discharge of the musketry in a running fire,
and huzza:

"'Long live the friendly European Powers!'

"This last discharge of thirteen pieces of artillery will be given, followed by a general running fire, and huzza:

"'The American States!'"

This program was executed with precision,
and the effect was brilliant and picturesque in
the extreme. A bright May sun was shining
overhead, new colors were flying and many of
the soldiers were attired in new uniforms.
Lafayette, and other French officers were present. Lord Stirling and General Green, with
their staff officers, took part in the celebration,
and ladies surrounded Mrs. Washington, and
viewed the spectacle.

In the afternoon General Washington invited
the officers and guests to a banquet, which was
greatly celebrated at the time. An eye witness
reports to a newspaper that the officers marched
to the amphitheater thirteen abreast, and arm in
arm.

Mrs. Washington, Mrs. Green, Lady Stirling
and her daughter, with many ladies of the neighborhood, graced the scene. Lafayette was in

the highest spirits, and triumphant joy shone in every countenance.

All over the land, as the news traveled from State to State and town to town, similar scenes of thanksgiving and festivity were repeated.

THE THANKSGIVING IN BOSTON HARBOR

HEZEKIAH BUTTERWORTH

" Praise ye the Lord!" The psalm to-day
   Still rises on our ears,
Borne from the hills of Boston Bay
   Through five times fifty years,
When Winthrop's fleet from Yarmouth crept
   Out to the open main,
And through the widening waters swept,
   In April sun and rain.
     " Pray to the Lord with fervent lips,"
      The leader shouted, " pray ";
     And prayer arose from all the ships
     As faded Yarmouth Bay.

They passed the Scilly Isles that day,
   And May-days came, and June,
And thrice upon the ocean lay
   The full orb of the moon.
And as that day, on Yarmouth Bay,
   Ere England sunk from view,

While yet the rippling Solent lay
  In April skies of blue,
    " Pray to the Lord with fervent lips,"
      Each morn was shouted, " pray ";
    And prayer arose from all the ships,
      As first in Yarmouth Bay;

Blew warm the breeze o'er Western seas,
  Through Maytime morns, and June,
Till hailed these souls the Isles of Shoals,
  Low 'neath the summer moon;
And as Cape Ann arose to view,
  And Norman's Woe they passed,
The wood-doves came the white mists
    through,
    And circled round each mast.
    " Pray to the Lord with fervent lips,"
      Then called the leader, " pray ";
    And prayer arose from all the ships,
      As first in Yarmouth Bay.

Above the sea the hill-tops fair —
  God's towers — began to rise,
And odors rare breathe through the air,
  Like balms of Paradise.
Through burning skies the ospreys flew,
  And near the pine-cooled shores
Danced airy boat and thin canoe,
  To flash of sunlit oars.
    " Pray to the Lord with fervent lips,"
      The leader shouted, " pray ! "

Then prayer arose, and all the ships
  Sailed into Boston Bay.

The white wings folded, anchors down,
  The sea-worn fleet in line,
Fair rose the hills where Boston town
  Should rise from clouds of pine;
Fair was the harbor, summit-walled,
  And placid lay the sea.
" Praise ye the Lord," the leader called;
  " Praise ye the Lord," spake he.
    " Give thanks to God with fervent lips,
      Give thanks to God to-day,"
    The anthem rose from all the ships,
      Safe moored in Boston Bay.

      *   *   *   *   *   *   *   *

Our fathers' prayers have changed to psalms,
  As David's treasures old
Turned, on the Temple's giant arms,
  To lily-work of gold.
Ho! vanished ships from Yarmouth's tide,
  Ho! ships of Boston Bay,
Your prayers have crossed the centuries wide
  To this Thanksgiving Day!
    We pray to God with fervent lips,
      We praise the Lord to-day,
    As prayers arose from Yarmouth ships,
      But psalms from Boston Bay.

II

CELEBRATION OF THANKS-GIVING

THE PUMPKIN.

J. G. WHITTIER

Oh! greenly and fair in the land of the sun,
The vines of the gourd and the rich melon run,
And the rock and the tree and the cottage en-
    fold
With broad leaves all greenness, and blossoms
    all gold,
Like that which o'er Nineveh's prophet once
    grew,
While we waited to know that his warning was
    true,
And longed for the storm cloud, and listened
    in vain
For the rush of the whirlwind and red fire of
    rain.

On the banks of the Xenil the dark Spanish
    maiden
Comes up with the fruit of the tangled vine
    laden;
And the Creole of Cuba laughs out to behold
Through orange leaves shining the broad
    spheres of gold;
Yet with dearer delight from his home from
    the north,

67

On the fields of his harvest the Yankee looks
forth,
Where crook-necks are circling and yellow
fruit shines,
And the sun of September melts down on his
vines.

Ah! on Thanksgiving Day, when from East and
from West,
From North and from South, come the pilgrim
and guest,
When the gray-haired New Englander sees
round his board
The old broken links of affection restored,
When the care-wearied man seeks his mother
once more,
And the worn mother smiles where the girl
smiled before —
What moistens the lip and what brightens the
eye?
What calls back the past like the rich pumpkin-
pie?

Oh, fruit loved of childhood! the old days re-
calling,
When wood grapes were purpling and brown
nuts were falling,
When wild, ugly faces we carved in its skin,
Glared out through the dark with a candle
within,

When we laughed round the corn-heap with
    hearts all in tune,
Our chair a broad pumpkin, our lantern the
    moon,
Telling tales of the fairy who traveled like
    steam,
In a pumpkin-shell coach with two rats for her
    team.

Then thanks for the present! none sweeter or
    better
E'er smoked from an oven or circled a platter!
Fairer hands never wrought at pastry more
    fine;
Brighter eyes never watched o'er its baking
    than thine;
And the prayer which my mouth is too full to
    express,
Swells my heart that thy shadow may never
    grow less,
That the days of thy lot may be lengthened be-
    low,
And the fame of thy worth like the pumpkin-
    vine grow,
And thy life be as sweet, and its last sunset
    sky
Golden-tinted and fair, as thy own pumpkin
    pie!

JERICHO BOB

ANNA EICHBERG KING

Jericho Bob, when he was four years old, hoped that one day he might be allowed to eat just as much turkey as he possibly could. He was eight now, but that hope had not been realized.

Mrs. Jericho Bob, his mother, kept hens for a living, and she expected that they would lay enough eggs in the course of time to help her son to an independent career as a bootblack.

They lived in a tumble-down house in a waste of land near the steam cars, and besides her hens Mrs. Bob owned a goat.

Our story has, however, nothing to do with the goat except to say he was there, and that he was on nibbling terms, not only with Jericho Bob, but with Bob's bosom friend, Julius Cæsar Fish, and it was surprising how many old hatbrims and other tidbits of clothing he could swallow during a day.

As Mrs. Bob truly said, it was no earthly use to get something new for Jericho, even if she could afford it; for the goat browsed all over him, and had been known to carry away even a leg of his trousers.

Jericho Bob was eight years old, and the friend of his bosom, Julius Cæsar Fish, was nine. They were so much alike that if it hadn't been for Jericho's bow-legs and his turn-up nose, you really could not have told them apart.

A kindred taste for turkey also united them.

In honor of Thanksgiving day Mrs. Bob always sacrificed a hen which would, but for such blessed release, have died of old age. One drumstick was given to Jericho, whose interior remained an unsatisfied void.

Jericho Bob had heard of turkey as a fowl larger, sweeter, and more tender than hen; and about Thanksgiving time he would linger around the provision stores and gaze with open mouth at the noble array of turkeys hanging head downward over bushels of cranberries, as if even at that uncooked stage, they were destined for one another. And turkey was his dream.

It was spring-time, and the hens were being a credit to themselves. The goat in the yard, tied to a stake, was varying a meal of old shoe and tomato-can by a nibble of fresh green grass. Mrs. Bob was laid up with rheumatism.

" Jericho Bob!" she said to her son, shaking her red and yellow turban at him, " Jericho Bob, you go down an' fetch de eggs to-day. Ef I find yer don't bring me twenty-three, I'll — well, never mind what I'll do, but yer won't like it."

Now, Jericho Bob meant to be honest, but the fact was he found twenty-four, and the twenty-fourth was so big, so remarkably big.

Twenty-three eggs he brought to Mrs. Bob, but the twenty-fourth he sinfully left in charge of the discreet hen.

On his return he met Julius Cæsar Fish, with his hands in his pockets and his head extinguished by his grandfather's fur cap.

Together they went toward the hen-coop, and Julius Cæsar Fish spoke, or rather lisped (he had lost some of his front teeth) :

" Jericho Bobth, tha'th a turkey'th egg."

" Yer don't say so? "

" I think i'th a-goin' ter hatch." No sooner said than they heard a pick and a peck in the shell.

" Pick! " a tiny beak broke through the shell. " Peck! " more beak. " Crack! " a funny little head, a long, bare neck, and then " Pick! peck! crack! " before them stood the funniest, fluffiest brown ball resting on two weak little legs.

" Hooray! " shouted the woolly heads.

" Peep! " said turkeykin.

" It's mine! " Jericho shouted excitedly.

" I'th Marm Pitkin'th turkey'th; she laid it there."

" It's mine, and I'm going to keep it, and next Thanksgiving I'm going ter eat him."

" Think your ma'll let you feed him up for thath? " Julius Cæsar asked triumphantly.

Jericho Bob's next Thanksgiving dinner seemed destined to be a dream. His face fell.

" I'll tell yer whath I'll do," his friend said, benevolently; " I'll keep'm for you, and Thanksgivin' we'll go halvth."

Jericho resigned himself to the inevitable, and the infant turkey was borne home by his friend.

Fish, Jr., lived next door, and the only difference in the premises was a freight-car permanently switched off before the broken-down fence of the Fish yard; and in this car turkeykin took up his abode.

I will not tell you how he grew and more than realized the hopes of his foster-fathers, nor with what impatience and anticipation they saw spring, summer, and autumn pass, while they watched their Thanksgiving dinner stalk proudly up the bare yard and even hop across the railroad tracks.

But, alas! the possession of the turkey brought with it strife and discord.

Quarrels arose between the friends as to the prospective disposal of his remains. We grieve to say that the question of who was to cook him led to blows.

It was the day before Thanksgiving. There was a coldness between the friends which was not dispelled by the bringing of a pint of cranberries to the common store by Jericho, and the contributing thereto of a couple of cold-boiled sweet potatoes by Julius Cæsar Fish.

The friends sat on an ancient wash-tub in the back yard, and there was a momentary truce between them. Before them stood the freight-car, and along the track beyond an occasional train tore down the road, which so far excited their mutual sympathy that they rose and shouted as one man.

At the open door of the freight-car stood the unsuspecting turkey and looked meditatively out on the landscape and at the two figures on the wash-tub.

One had bow-legs, a turn-up nose and a huge straw hat. The other wore a fur cap and a gentleman's swallow-tail coat, with the tails caught up because they were too long.

The turkey hopped out of the car and gazed confidingly at his protectors. In point of size he was altogether their superior.

" I think," said Jericho Bob, " we'd better ketch 'im. To-morrow's Thanksgiving. Yum! "

And he looked with great joy at the innocent, the unsuspecting fowl.

" Butcher Tham 'th goin' ter kill 'im for uth," Julius Cæsar hastened to say, " an' I kin cook 'im."

" No, you aint. I'm goin' to cook 'im," Jericho Bob cried, resentfully. " He's mine."

" He ainth; he'th mine."

"He was my egg," and Jericho Bob danced defiance at his friend.

The turkey looked on with some surprise, and he became alarmed when he saw his foster-fathers clasped in an embrace more of anger than of love.

"I'll eat 'im all alone!" Jericho Bob cried.

"No, yer sha'n't!" the other shouted.

The turkey shrieked in terror and fled in a circle about the yard.

"Now, look yere," said Julius Cæsar, who had conquered, "we're goin' to be squar'. He wath your egg, but who brought 'im up? Me! Who'th got a friend to kill 'im? Me! Who'th got a fire to cook 'im? Me! Now you git up and we'll kitch 'im. Ef you thay another word about your egg I'll jeth eat 'im up all mythelf."

Jericho Bob was conquered. With mutual understanding they approached the turkey.

"Come yere; come yere," Julius Cæsar said, coaxingly.

For a moment the bird gazed at both, uncertain what to do.

"Come yere," Julius Cæsar repeated, and made a dive for him. The turkey spread his tail. Oh! didn't he run.

"Now I've got yer!" the wicked Jericho Bob cried, and thought he had captured the fowl, when with a shriek from Jericho Bob, as the turkey knocked him over, the Thanksgiving dinner spread his wings, rose in the air, and alighted on the roof of the freight-car.

The turkey looked down over the edge of the car at his enemies, and they gazed up at him. Both parties surveyed the situation.

"We've got him," Julius Cæsar cried at last, exultantly. "You git on the roof, and ef you don't kitch 'im up thar, I'll kitch 'im down yere."

With the help of the wash-tub, an old chair, Julius Cæsar's back, and much scrambling, Jericho Bob was hoisted on top of the car. The turkey was stalking solemnly up and down the roof with tail and wings half spread.

"I've got yer now," Jericho Bob said, creeping softly after him. "I've got yer now, sure," he was just repeating, when with a deafening roar the express train for New York came tearing down the road.

For what possible reason it slowed up on approaching the freight-car nobody ever knew, but the fact remains that it did just as Jericho Bob laid his wicked black paw on the turkey's tail.

The turkey shrieked, spread his wings, shook the small black boy's grasp from his tail, and with a mighty swoop alighted on the roof of the very last car as it passed, and in a moment more Jericho Bob's Thanksgiving dinner had vanished, like a beautiful dream, down the road.

What became of that Thanksgiving dinner

no one ever knew. If you happen to meet a traveling turkey without any luggage, but with a smile on his countenance, please send word to Jericho Bob.

――――

A THANKSGIVING FABLE

OLIVER HERFORD

It was a hungry pussy cat, upon Thanksgiving
    morn,
And she watched a thankful little mouse, that
    ate an ear of corn.
" If I ate that thankful little mouse, how thank-
    ful he should be,
When he has made a meal himself, to make a
    meal for me!
" Then with his thanks for having fed, and his
    thanks for feeding me,
With all *his* thankfulness inside, how thankful I
    shall be!"
Thus mused the hungry pussy cat, upon Thanks-
    giving Day;
But the little mouse had overheard and declined
    (with thanks) to stay.

――――

THANKSGIVING

PHOEBE CARY

O men, grown sick with toil and care,
    Leave for awhile the crowded mart;

O women, sinking with despair,
  Weary of limb and faint of heart,
Forget your years to-day and come
As children back to childhood's home.

Follow again the winding rills,
  Go to the places where you went
When, climbing up the summer hills,
  In their green laps you sat content,
And softly leaned your head to rest
On Nature's calm and peaceful breast.

Walk through the sere and fading wood,
  So slightly trodden by your feet,
When all you knew of life was good,
  And all you dreamed of life was sweet,
And ever fondly looking back
O'er youthful love's enchanted track

Taste the ripe fruits from the orchard boughs.
  Drink from the mossy well once more,
Breathe fragrance from the crowded mows
  With fresh, sweet clover running o'er,
And count the treasures at your feet,
Of silver rye and golden wheat.

Go sit beside the hearth again,
  Whose circle once was glad and gay;
And if, from out the precious chain,
  Some shining links have dropped away,
Then guard with tender heart and hand
The remnant of thy household band.

Draw near the board with plenty spread,
　　And if, in the accustomed place,
You see the father's reverend head,
　　Or mother's patient, loving face,
Whate'er your life may have of ill,
Thank God that these are left you still.

And though where home has been you stand
　　To-day in alien loneliness;
Though you may clasp no brother's hand,
　　And claim no sister's tender kiss;
Though with no friend nor lover nigh,
The past is all your company,

Thank God for friends your life has known,
　　For every dear, departed day;
The blessed past is safe alone —
　　God gives, but does not take away;
He only safely keeps above
For us the treasures that we love.

———

THANKSGIVING DAY

LYDIA MARIA CHILD

Over the river and through the wood,
　　To grandfather's house we go;
　　　The horse knows the way
　　　To carry the sleigh
　　Through the white and drifted snow.

Over the river and through the wood —
　Oh, how the wind does blow!
　　It stings the toes
　　And bites the nose,
　As over the ground we go.

Over the river and through the wood,
　To have a first-rate play.
　　Hear the bells ring,
　　" Ting-a-ling-ding!"
　Hurrah for Thanksgiving Day!

Over the river and through the wood
　Trot fast, my dapple-gray!
　　Spring over the ground,
　　Like a hunting-hound!
　For this is Thanksgiving Day.

Over the river and through the wood,
　And straight through the barn-yard gate.
　　We seem to go
　　Extremely slow,—
　It is so hard to wait!

Over the river and through the wood —
　Now grandmother's cap I spy!
　　Hurrah for the fun!
　　Is the pudding done?
　Hurrah for the pumpkin-pie!

'WORK AND PLAY IN LEYDEN'

WILLIAM ELLIOT GRIFFIS

* * * * * *

Most popular and interesting of all the single festivals — for the Kermiss, or universal merrymaking, lasted a week — was the annual Thanksgiving Day on October 3, when all the Dutch people of the city went to church to thank God for deliverance from the enemy and for his mercies, and then returned home to eat their favorite historic dish,— a stew of meat and vegetables, Spanish hodge-podge, or hutch-putch, as they called it,— in memory of their fathers. To this dish they added dainties and rich things for joy and gladness. Thus the Pilgrims had before them a living example, which they could never forget, of an annual Thanksgiving Day to God. Like equally sacred commemorative days in America and in all the world, perhaps, the mode of celebration became after a few generations less rigidly religious.

* * * * * *

THANKSGIVING PHILOSOPHY

CHARLOTTE W. THURSTON

" Hiss! Hiss!" said the Goose, " they've taken
us three

83

To fatten for Christmas — such songsters as
   we!
I'll be tough as a goose! It's a sin and a
   shame
Be wise, Mister Turkey, and you'll do the same.
        Hiss!" said the Goose,
         "I call it abuse!"
         "Quack!" said the Duck,
         "I call it good luck!
Just think of the dainties they give us to eat —
Such apple-cores, squash-seeds, and gristles of
   meat!
Let's be off for a lunch; see how fast I can
   hobble."
But the Turkey only answered with a
         "Gobble! gobble! gobble!"

"Hiss! Hiss!" said the Goose, "'tis a sad want
   of luck!
You don't know a thing; you're a goose of a
   duck!
A regular quack,— you haven't any brains;
You don't know enough to go in when it rains."
        "Quack!" said the Duck,
        "'Tis a world of good luck!"
        "Hiss!" said the Goose,
        "'Tis a world of abuse!"
"Quack! quack!" said the Duck, "what a
   great goose you are."
"Hiss!" shrilled the Goose, till you heard her
   afar,

" Hiss! Mister Turkey, the world is full of
    trouble."
But the Turkey only answered with a
              " Gobble! gobble! gobble! "

———

THANKSGIVING DINNERS

FROM 'OLD TIME CHILD LIFE'

E. H. ARR

Farmer Lathem used to say that the weather was "set in its ways," and that the ground always "shut up" about Thanksgiving-time. All northern country-livers know what that shutting up means. Jack Frost flirts weeks beforehand in and out shady corners, while the splendor of field and forest deludes no one by its hectic outburst of coloring. To-day's sunshine melts the rime of the past night; but it is in nowise to be depended upon. In vain the housewife blankets her flower-beds. To-morrow she wakes up to find only little heart-shaped bare spots in the corners of her window-panes, through which she looks out upon a frozen landscape. Every leaf is gangrened, and every twig is as positive as an exclamation-point: "The ground has shut up!"

Then follows that newborn indoor-life which, if well regulated, is like a smooth-flowing pastoral, with here and there a quickening of its rhythm. In the first autumnal freedom of this life from care, is offered up that thanksgiving

which has become a part of the history of New
England. In early times the religious fervor
of Thanksgiving-Day was far greater than now.
When the gathered fruits of the earth poured
into store-rooms and cellars, the hearts of simple ancient workers poured out in grateful worship. With lapse of years family ties broad-
ened, substance waxed fat, and by degrees the
thanksgiving, preceded by much slaughter, became what an old Puritan would have looked
upon as a half-heathen rite. With all due def-
erence, however, to the sweet piety with which
these same Puritans observed it, I must confess
that it is the flavor of smoking fleshpots — not
that of strong sermons — which has come down
to me from my childhood Thanksgivings.

Next to the religious aspect of this day, its
best essence has always been its hospitality. It
is the home-rallying point of disintegrated families,— the altar from which the incense of affection goes up with that of baked meats, and
kindleth anew from its yearly gathering of
forces. " Going home to Thanksgiving " is the
watchword of many old New England families;
and with them, for that day at least, the cur-
rent of love flows backward to the fathers and
mothers and the dear old grandparents, who sit
waiting by ancestral hearths.

Were the Thanksgiving dinners of yester-
day,— were they better than any dinners of to-
day? or are they relished by the piquant sauces

of indulgent memory? I think the dinners were in every way better,— better in material, in make-up, in baking, and in serving. The sweet, firm fibre of their flesh and fowl had been fed upon sun-ripened grain and fruits. Their toothsome condiments and mixtures were the work of the skilled housewife, who, when her viands were ready, had a brick oven to cook and brown them in as she willed.

For skill of engineering what could surpass one of these dinners, built up by a great deal of work done on a side-track? In Whitefield Corner children helped chop the mince-meat, and, under sharp maternal eye, stoned the raisins. The oven quietly swallowed up and as quietly disgorged. Save by unusually sweet odors much of the previous preparation hardly betrayed itself. But on Thanksgiving-Day, what hidden secrets of pantry and closet were revealed! The dinner — in reality the condensed result of many days of intelligent, persistent labor — passed smoking hot from the oven to the table; gravies and sauces glided in by side-doors; pickles took their places, and the oldtime boy was as deaf to the grace as he had been to the previous sermon. He foolishly gave no heed to the dear mother's often-repeated suggestion that the dinner had just begun. He ate freely, slighted the chicken-pie because of a squabble of a wish-bone which, undried, refused to break. The pudding proved to be what was called "filling"; and I do not believe that a middle-aged, country-born New Englander lives who does not recall the exquisite pang with which, in childhood, a semicircle of Thanksgiving pie was sometimes left upon the plate. A small girl, or boy, was seldom unequal to an after-dash at raisins and nuts, and never can die out of memory that supreme air of contentment which used, from the dear old grandmother down to the youngest child, to settle upon a family after it had partaken of a Thanksgiving dinner.

Thankfulness took the form of rest. The old people dozed, careful householder and busy matron let go the reins of care, and children dreamily floated through the afternoon hours of this memorial day. Nature herself seemed to abet their mood, and to mellow the atmosphere both indoors and out. The happy season was lengthened by withholding of candles, and the brightness of sunset filled the room like a benediction.

Better still, the beautiful afterglow of innocent social life, of which the grandfather and grandmother were the centre, when nuts and apples were brought in and talk pleasantly took the form of reminiscence.

Best of all, that sweet and tender parting, when, in the later evening, the dear old folks sped the little ones with their blessing, and, crowned by the ruddy firelight, fore-shadowed to these, the loitering young lovers, their own coming glory.

When I say that the material of the oldtime country Thanksgiving dinner was better than that of a like dinner of to-day, I know whereof I affirm. So much in my childhood did the best yearly products of the earth converge into Thanksgiving-Day that it became to country boys a sort of fetich, to which objects were dedicated long beforehand with the prefix of Thanksgiving. Every thirfty home had its Thanksgiving turkey and pullets and pig set aside for careful tending, at the slaughter of which the young barbarians were always ready to lend a helping hand. They had their own especial wild-forage offerings, such as sweet flag and nuts. They loved the previous mysteries and bustle of the day, and the wonder is that out of so much carnal entanglement of it they could carry into mature life, as they did, its pure, vivifying sentiment of heavenly worship and family love.

Close upon it, Whitefield farmers used to prowl, lantern in hand, in and out barns and sheds, after unwary fowl, whose fatness had marked them weeks beforehand for the sacrificial knife. What tidbits went, day by day, into the rounding-out of such Thanksgiving turkeys, geese, and pullets as made gourmands out of the eaters of them! How clean and innocent looked the inevitable, disembowelled pig, which, with its flakes of white fat, hung, at the right season, before almost every farmer's door! The roast of this pig known, when served at a Thanksgiving dinner, as sparerib, had been fattened upon buttermilk and. cornmeal. Its best relish could be gotten by taking it on the sly, rib by rib, between thumb and finger, and dexterously sucking its inmost juices. Sweeter meat than that next its bone is nowhere to be found. As my grandmother used to say of the crust of her johnny-cakes, into every fibre of it seemed to have gone the golden glory of the corn.

I am just as positive about the cooking as I am about the material of the dinners. The relish of the oldtime mince-pies has quite passed into tradition,— those pies upon which our stalwart ancestors throve, and with which they regaled their guests. They have been decried because they have been misunderstood. They were the product of the skilled labor of the housewife, not the experiment of the hand-maiden. Hence they have to be largely a thing of the past. Baked in brick ovens they were no more like the thin, stove-dried dyspepsia-giving abortions sold in shops, than the Thanksgiving pig fed by a farmer's wife upon milk and meal, is like the poisonous swine driven through city streets.

An impression, in some localities, seems to prevail that New England people have been, and still are, largely fed upon pies. The diet has also been strongly condemned as unhealthful. It may be so; still, with my own recollections of them, I should be in a state of daily thanksgiving if there could as often appear upon my table one of my grandmother's delicious pies.

A true Thanksgiving mince-pie should be an inch thick, with a thin, flaky crust, tinted by its imprisoned juices, which threaten to break through like blood from overfull veins. Around its edge must be a slight crinkle made by the tines of a fork or castor-bottle cover; and in its top a hole here and there from the stroke of a knife to let the steam out. This steam, once known, can never be forgotten,— the intermingled exhalation of beef and pork or suet, and apples and raisins and citron and sugar and spices and boiled cider, and, in profane families, of a dash of good brandy. When you press upon its upper crust, there should gush up from the slashes a brown gravy, sparkling with tiny globules of fat, and deliciously scenting the room. Fortunate they who have been permitted to relish, with a slice of cream cheese, and a mug of sweet cider, this healthful, bliss-giving pie!

How, as I talk about such common things, the fashioners of them come back to me! It is like opening the door to a gallery of old portraits, from out whose dim perspective wrin-

kled hands beckon to me; and, because I will
it, lead me to oldtime thanksgiving altars,—
altars before which ministered simple-hearted,
unveneered, godly people, and whose smoking
incense has been filtered by time into a fragrant
memory. Indeed, the glory of Thanksgiving-
Day is that heart, that core of it, which under-
lies all outer crust of worldliness. It is born
of, and takes hold utterly, of family-life.
Hence one is miserly of such customs of it, be
they ever so homely, as pleasantly link him or
her with the past.

A little more than forty years ago I went,
late one afternoon, with my grandmother, to
visit Mrs. Merrill, who lived at the top of Merrill's Hill, in the town of East Road, the woman
of whom I borrowed the rennet. It was the
day before Thanksgiving, and Mrs. Merrill,
with her daughter and her sister, was busy
making mince-pies. She was a plump, rosy-
cheeked, spry little woman,— the best kind of
a figure to put in the foreground of a *genre*
picture. Hanging from a crane in the kitchen
fireplace was a steaming pot full of mince-meat,
which Mrs. Merrill stirred with a spoon and
dipped into crusted plates, passed to her by her
daughter, Josephine,— a tall, thin, tallowy-
faced girl, expert at cutting off superfluous pie-
crust by running a knife rapidly around the
edge of a plate. Before a table stood Mrs.
Merrill's sister, rolling out little pats of crust,

sliced from a flaky lump into thin leaves, which
she folded and then unfolded upon the plates
as they shifted through Josephine's hands to
the pot. The passes were made so quickly that
they seemed almost like sleight-of-hand. The
pies were baked in batches, and just after we
went in the sister took one batch out of the
oven and put in another.

At first Mrs. Merrill proposed to go with us
into the " foreroom," but my grandmother told
her to " keep right on with her work," which
she seemed glad to do, as the heat of her oven
she said had gotten low and must be " brisked
up with coals."

I sat and watched and listened to these
women. They talked much of pies and the
mysteries of their making. Mrs. Merrill told
us that " father " (meaning Mr. Merrill) had
bought his raisins at West instead of East
Road ; and though they were a cent higher on
a pound, they were not so good as those of the
year before. Her boiled cider was also less
strong than usual, hence she feared for the
quality of her pies. She offered a taste of her
meat to my grandmother, who smacked her lips,
and told Mrs. Merrill that she must be " fishing for a compliment," for no better meat than
hers ever " went into a pie." Then they all
praised the color of it, and my grandmother
handed the half-filled spoon over to me, which
I lapped quite clean.

Mrs. Merrill told us, in confidence, that she should have put a little " spirit " into her meat, had she not been afraid that it would " go against the grain " of her sister's husband, who was a minister,— one of the " called kind," and " a master-hand," she declared, " at a revival." One was " going on," she said, then, at West Road, and she could not see what made her Josephine so " stiff-necked." The pies were for early winter use. " Father " had put up a hanging-shelf for them in the garret, out of the way of mice, and she did hope they would " taste like something."

When it grew dark she told Josephine to " light up," and the " tallow-dip " only brought out into sharp-cut silhouette these quaint workers at their homely task. The fire glowed, the pot sputtered, the pies were shaped and baked, the women prattled. Then the father and the preacher came in, both stalwart and good-natured. The crane was swung back, Josephine lighted up the " foreroom," and shortly my grandmother went home. I left the actual scene behind me, but the picturesqueness, the spirit of it, brought out by firelight, is immortal.

Dear old workers, with your dear old ways, my pen lingers lovingly over you. I remember perfectly how, as I went out from them to the top of Merrill's Hill, the sharp peaks of a distant mountain range stood out against the sky,

which was red with the afterglow of sunset,—
rugged yet beautiful. Just so, in the afterglow of life, stand out in memory such customs, with their experiences, as took root in the
sources of rational enjoyment.

THANKSGIVIN' PUMPKIN PIES

MARGARET SANGSTER

So you bid me to Thanksgivin'! Thank you,
    neighbor, it is kind,
To keep a plain old body like myself so much
    in mind;
Here I've been sittin' all alone, and a mist be-
    fore my eyes,
A-thinkin', like a simpleton, of mother's pump-
    kin pies.

Yes, I've just come home from Sarah's; come
    home I'm glad to say;
And here, God helping me, I mean in future
    time to stay;
Oh! Sarah's folks are very fine, but I felt all at
    sea,
And though the rooms were 'mazin' big, they
    seemed too small for me.

The house is like a palace, and mine's a tiny
    nest,

But, neighbor, I'm contented here, I like this
    place the best;
Just as Sarah's creams and salads I don't know
    how to prize;
Her French cook costs a fortune, but *I* favor
    home-made pies,

Like mother's; flaky, rich and brown, and
    toothsome with the spice;
I grew to loathe her dinners, cut in half with
    lemon ice:
Give me good food, biled greens and pork, and
    turkey now and then;
I tell you on our mountain fare we've raised a
    race of *men*.

Not spindlin' like them city folks, in dress-suits
    if you please,
An, mincin' in their low-cut shoes, an' bowin'
    to their knees.
I hate such silly airs; I like to hear a hearty
    word;
No! I'm not deaf, but when one speaks, why,
    speak so's to be heard.

In Sarah's house 'twas "aunty this" and
    "aunty that," until
I saw I made a discord, let me do my best; 'an
    still
I'm sure the child loves aunty, but, neighbor,
    she and I

Are far apart and nohow could our ways again
    draw nigh.

She wears her black silk every day, a-trailin'
    on the ground,
Leastwise, a-trailin' on the *floor;* 'tis called, I
    b'lieve, tea-gowned,
An' frills an' lace, 'an hot-house flowers; such
    waste, it worried me,
Rememberin' Jotham Peckham's kin, as poor
    as poor could be.

Rememberin' Jotham Peckham, I was vexed to
    see his child,
A-throwin' money here and there; it made me
    fairly wild.
Her house, it's just like Barnum's, with jim-
    cracks everywhere,
When pa and me the children took to see the
    wonders there.

How I run on! Well, thank you, neighbor; I
    see you want to go;
I'm comin' to Thanksgivin'; your good old
    ways I know.
An' my mouth waters, dear old friend, there's
    tears in these dim eyes,
For I shall taste the flavor of mother's pumpkin
    pies.

And though I'm 'most threescore and ten, an'
    cranky, I'm afraid,

Once more I'll feel myself a child, my mother's
    little maid;
And I'll be *very* pleased to help, in any way I
    can;
Good-bye, dear, and my love to Ruth; a kiss to
    Mary Ann.

———

THANKSGIVING

HANNAH E. GAREY

Come forth, come forth, to the festal board,
    As our sires were wont in the days of old;
The reapers are home with their harvest hoard,
    The herds have hied to their wintry fold,
And the cullers of fruit our vaults have stored
    With the wealth of the orchard's freight of
    gold.

Come forth, come forth, with your heart-felt
    praise,
    To swell the songs at the altar's side;
For a lofty pæan to God we raise,
    Who hath scattered His love gifts free and
    wide,
And still, from the wan earth's earliest days,
    His seed-time and harvest hath not denied.

   *   *   *   *   *   *   *   *

We hallow the day as our fathers did,
    With a mingling of gladness and praise
    and prayer,

With a willing boon for the lowliest shed,
 That the hungry and poor in our thanks
  may share,
And the scantiest table be freely spread,
 And the lip of the mourner a blessing bear.

For the sons of the feeble pilgrim band
 Who on a distant rock-bound bay
Gave thanks for the gifts of the teeming land.
 Have spread over mountain and stream
  away;
And a song of praise shall to God ascend
 From a myriad burning lips to-day.

Come forth, come forth, with the chiming bell,
 A joyous throng to the altar's side;
Come mingle your tones with the organ's swell;
 And, where the door of the feast stands
  wide,
Let the gray-haired sire to his grandchild tell
 A tale of our nation's grateful pride.

———

ANN MARY

HER TWO THANKSGIVINGS

"Grandma."

"What is it, child?"

"You goin' to put that cup-cake into the pan to bake it now, grandma?"

"Yes; I guess so. It's beat 'bout enough."

"You ain't put in a mite of nutmeg, grandma."

The grandmother turned around to Ann Mary.

"Don't you be quite so anxious," said she, with sarcastic emphasis. "I allers put the nutmeg in cup-cake the very last thing. I rather guess I shouldn't have put this cake into the oven without nutmeg!"

The old woman beat fiercely on the cake. She used her hand instead of a spoon, and she held the yellow mixing-bowl poised on her hip under her arm. She was stout and rosy-faced. She had crinkly white hair, and she always wore a string of gold beads around her creasy neck. She never took off the gold beads except to put them under her pillow at night, she was so afraid of their being stolen. Old Mrs.

Little had always been nervous about thieves, although none had ever troubled her.

"You may go into the pantry, an' bring out the nutmeg now, Ann Mary," said she presently, with dignity.

Ann Mary soberly slipped down from her chair and went. She realized that she had made a mistake. It was quite an understood thing for Ann Mary to have an eye upon her grandmother while she was cooking, to be sure that she put in everything that she should, and nothing that she should not, for the old woman was absent-minded. But it had to be managed with great delicacy, and the corrections had to be quite irrefutable, or Ann Mary was reprimanded for her pains.

When Ann Mary had deposited the nutmeg-box and the grater at her grandmother's elbow, she took up her station again. She sat at a corner of the table in one of the high kitchen-chairs. Her feet could not touch the floor, and they dangled uneasily in their stout leather shoes, but she never rested them on the chair round, nor even swung them by way of solace. Ann Mary's grandmother did not like to have her chair rounds all marked up by shoes, and swinging feet disturbed her while she was cooking. Ann Mary sat up, grave and straight. She was a delicate, slender little girl, but she never stooped. She had an odd resemblance to her grandmother; a resemblance more of manner than of feature. She held back her narrow shoulders in the same determined way in which the old woman held her broad ones; she walked as she did, and spoke as she did.

Mrs. Little was very proud of Ann Mary Evans; Ann Mary was her only daughter's child, and had lived with her grandmother ever since she was a baby. The child could not remember either her father or mother, she was so little when they died.

Ann Mary was delicate, so she did not go to the village to the public school. Miss Loretta Adams, a young lady who lived in the neighborhood, gave her lessons. Loretta had graduated in a beautiful white muslin dress at the high school over in the village, and Ann Mary had a great respect and admiration for her. Loretta had a parlor-organ, and could play on it, and she was going to give Ann Mary lessons after Thanksgiving. Just now there was a vacation. Loretta had gone to Boston to spend two weeks with her cousin.

Ann Mary was all in brown, a brown calico dress and a brown calico, long-sleeved apron; and her brown hair was braided in two tight little tails that were tied with some old brown bonnet-strings of Mrs. Little's, and flared out stiffly behind the ears. Once, when Ann Mary was at her home, Loretta Adams had taken it upon herself to comb out the tight braids and set the hair flowing in a fluffy mass over the shoulders; but when Ann Mary came home her grandmother was properly indignant. She seized her and re-braided the tails with stout and painful jerks. "I ain't goin' to have Loretty Adams meddlin' with your hair," said she, "an' she can jest understand it. If she wants to have her own hair all in a frowzle, an' look like a wild Injun, she can; you sha'n't!"

And Ann Mary, standing before her grandmother with head meekly bent and watery eyes, decided that she would have to tell Loretta that she musn't touch the braids, if she proposed it again.

That morning, while Mrs. Little was making the pies, and the cake, and the pudding, Ann Mary was sitting idle, for her part of the Thanksgiving cooking was done. She had worked so fast the day before and early that morning that she had the raisins all picked over and seeded, and the apples pared and sliced; and that was about all that her grandmother thought she could do. Ann Mary herself was of a different opinion; she was twelve years old, if she *was* small for her age, and she considered herself quite capable of making pies and cup-cake.

However, it was something to sit there at the table and have that covert sense of superintending her grandmother, and to be reasonably sure that some of the food would have a strange flavor were it not for her vigilance.

Mrs. Little's mince-pies had all been baked
the day before; to-day, as she said, she was
"making apple and squash." While the apple-
pies were in progress, Ann Mary watched her
narrowly. Her small folded hands twitched
and her little neck seemed to elongate above
her apron; but she waited until her grandmother took up an upper crust, and was just
about to lay it over a pie. Then she spoke up
suddenly. Her voice had a timid yet assertive
chirp like a bird's.

"Grandma!"

"Well, what is it, child?"

"You goin' to put that crust on that pie
now, grandma?"

Mrs. Little stood uneasily reflective. She
eyed the pie sharply. "Yes, I be. Why?"
she returned, in a doubtful yet defiant manner.

"You haven't put one bit of sugar in."

"For the land sakes!" Mrs. Little did not
take correction of this kind happily, but when
she was made to fairly acknowledge the need
of it, she showed no resentment. She laid the
upper crust back on the board and sweetened
the pie. Ann Mary watched her gravely, but
she was inwardly complacent. After she had
rescued the pudding from being baked without
the plums, and it was nearly dinner-time, her
grandfather came home. He had been over to
the village to buy the Thanksgiving turkey.
Ann Mary looked out wth delight when he

drove past the windows on his way to the barn.

"Grandpa's got home," said she.

It was snowing quite hard, and she saw the old man and the steadily tramping white horse and the tilting wagon through a thick mist of falling snow-flakes.

Before Mr. Little came into the kitchen, his wife warned him to be sure to wipe all the snow from his feet, and not to track in any, so he stamped vigorously out in the shed. Then he entered with an air of pride. "There!" said he, "what do ye think of that for a turkey?" Mr. Little was generally slow and gentle in his ways, but to-day he was quite excited over the turkey. He held it up with considerable difficulty. He was a small old man, and the cords on his lean hands knotted. "It weighs a good fifteen pound'," said he, "an' there wasn't a better one in the store. Adkins didn't have a very big lot on hand."

"I should think that was queer, the day before Thanksgivin'," said Mrs. Little. She was examining the turkey critically. "I guess it'll do," she declared finally. That was her highest expression of approbation. "Well, I rayther thought you'd think so," rejoined the old man, beaming. "I guess it's about as good a one as can be got — they said 'twas, down there. Sam White he was in there, and he said 'twas; he said I was goin' to get it in

pretty good season for Thanksgivin'," said
Mrs. Little.

"Well, I don't think 'twas, nuther. I didn't
see jest what Sam meant by it."

Ann Mary was dumb with admiration.
When the turkey was laid on the broad shelf
in the pantry, she went and gazed upon it. In
the afternoon there was great enjoyment seeing it stuffed and made ready for the oven.
Indeed, this day was throughout one of great
enjoyment, being full of the very aroma of
festivity and good cheer and gala times, and
even sweeter than the occasion which it preceded. Ann Mary had only one damper all
day, and that was the non-arrival of a letter.
Mrs. Little had invited her son and his family
to spend Thanksgiving, but now they probably
were not coming, since not a word in reply had
been received. When Mr. Little said there
was no letter in the post-office, Ann Mary's
face fell. "Oh, dear," said she, "don't you
suppose Lucy will come, grandma?"

"No," replied her grandmother, "I don't.
Edward never did such a thing as not to send
no word when he was comin', in his life, nor
Maria neither. I ain't no idee they'll come."

"Oh, dear!" said Ann Mary again.

"Well, you'll have to make up your mind
to it," returned her grandmother. She was
sore over her own disappointment, and so was
irascible towards Ann Mary's. "It's no worse

for you than for the rest of us. I guess you can keep one Thanksgivin' without Lucy."

For a while it almost seemed to Ann Mary that she could not. Lucy was her only cousin. She loved Lucy dearly, and she was lonesome for another little girl; nobody knew how she had counted upon seeing her cousin. Ann Mary herself had a forlorn hope that Lucy still might come, even if Uncle Edward *was* always so particular about sending word, and no word had been received. On Thanksgiving morning she kept running to the window and looking down the road. But when the stage from the village came, it passed right by the house without slackening its speed.

Then there was no hope left at all.

"You might jest as well be easy," said her grandmother. "I guess you can have a good Thanksgivin' if Lucy *ain't* here. This evenin' you can ask Loretty to come over a little while, if you want to, an' you can make some nut-candy."

"Loretta ain't at home."

"She'll come home for Thanksgivin', I guess. It ain't very likely she's stayed away over that. When I get the dinner ready to take up, you can carry a plateful down to Sarah Bean's, an' that'll be somethin' for you to do, too. I guess you can manage."

Thanksgiving Day was a very pleasant day,

although there was considerable snow on the
ground, for it had snowed all the day before.
Mr. Little and Ann Mary did not go to church
as usual, on that account.

The old man did not like to drive to the village before the roads were beaten out. Mrs.
Little lamented not a little over it. It was the
custom for her husband and granddaughter to
attend church Thanksgiving morning, while
she stayed at home and cooked the dinner.
"It does seem dreadful heathenish for nobody
to go to meetin' Thanksgivin' Day," said she;
"an' we ain't even heard the proclamation
read, neither. It rained so hard last Sabbath
that we couldn't go."

The season was unusually wintry and severe,
and lately the family had been prevented from
church-going. It was two Sundays since any
of the family had gone. The village was three
miles away, and the road was rough. Mr. Little was too old to drive over it in very bad
weather.

When Ann Mary went to carry the plate of
Thanksgiving dinner to Sarah Bean, she wore
a pair of her grandfather's blue woollen socks
drawn over her shoes to keep out the snow.
The snow was rather deep for easy walking,
but she did not mind that. She carried the
dinner with great care; there was a large plate
well filled, and a tin dish was turned over it to

keep it warm. Sarah Bean was an old woman who lived alone. Her house was about a quarter of a mile from the Littles'.

When Ann Mary reached the house, she found the old woman making a cup of tea. There did not seem to be much of anything but tea and bread-and-butter for her dinner. She was very deaf and infirm, all her joints shook when she tried to use them, and her voice quavered when she talked. She took the plate, and her hands trembled so that the tin dish played on the plate like a clapper. "Why," said she, overjoyed, "this looks just like Thanksgiving Day, tell your grandma!"

"Why, it *is* Thanksgiving Day," declared Ann Mary, with some wonder.

"What?" asked Sarah Bean.

"*It is Thanksgiving Day, you know.*" But it was of no use, the old woman could not hear a word. Ann Mary's voice was too low.

Ann Mary could not walk very fast on account of the snow. She was absent some three-quarters of an hour; her grandmother had told her that dinner would be all on the table when she returned. She was enjoying the nice things in anticipation all the day; when she came near the house, she could smell roasted turkey, and there was also a sweet spicy odor in the air.

She noticed with surprise that a sleigh had been in the yard. "I wonder who's come," she said to herself. She thought of Lucy, and whether they *could* have driven over from the village. She ran in. "Why, who's come?" she cried out.

Her voice sounded like a shout in her own ears; it seemed to awaken echoes. She fairly startled herself, for there was no one in the room. There was absolute quiet through all the house. There was even no sizzling from the kettles on the stove, for everything had been dished up. The vegetables, all salted and peppered and buttered, were on the table — but the turkey was not there. In the great vacant place where the turkey should have been was a piece of white paper. Ann Mary spied it in a moment. She caught it up and looked at it. It was a note from her grandmother:

> We have had word that Aunt Betsey has had a bad turn. Lizz wants us to come. The dinner is all ready for you. If we ain't home to-night, you can get Loretty to stay with you. Be a good girl.
>
> GRANDMA.

Ann Mary read the note and stood reflecting, her mouth drooping at the corners. Aunt Betsey was Mrs. Little's sister; Lizz was her daughter who lived with her and took care of her. They lived in Derby, and Derby was fourteen miles away. It seemed a long distance to Ann Mary, and she felt sure that her grandparents could not come home that night. She looked around the empty room and sighed. After a while she sat down and pulled off the snowy socks; she thought she might as well eat her dinner, although she did not feel so hungry as she had expected. Everything was on the table but the turkey and plum-pudding. Ann Mary supposed these were in the oven keeping warm; the door was ajar. But, when she looked, they were not there either. It was very strange; there were the dripping-pan in which the turkey had been baked, on the back of the stove, with some gravy in it; and there was the empty pudding-dish on the hearth.

"What has grandma done with the turkey and the plum-pudding?" said Ann Mary, aloud.

She looked again in the pantry; then she went down cellar — there seemed to be so few places in the house in which it was reasonable to search for a turkey and a plum-pudding!

Finally she gave it up, and sat down to dinner. There was plenty of squash and potatoes and turnips and onions and beets and cranberry-sauce and pies; but it was no Thanksgiving dinner without turkey and plum-pudding. It was like a great flourish of accompaniment without any song.

Ann Mary did as well as she could; she put some turkey-gravy on her potato and filled up her plate with vegetables; but she did not enjoy the dinner. She felt more and more lonely, too. She resolved that after she had washed up the dinner dishes and changed her dress, she would go over to Loretta Adams'. It was quite a piece of work, washing the dinner dishes, there were so many pans and kettles; it was the middle of the afternoon when she finished. Then Ann Mary put on her best plaid dress, and tied her best ribbons on her braids, and it was four o'clock before she started for Loretta's.

Loretta lived in a white cottage about half a mile away towards the village. The front yard had many bushes in it, and the front path was bordered with box; the bushes were now mounds of snow, and the box was indicated by two snowy ridges.

The house had a shut-up look; the sitting-room curtains were down. Ann Mary went around to the side door; but it was locked. Then she went up the front walk between the snowy ridges of box, and tried the front door; that also was locked. The Adamses had gone away. Ann Mary did not know what to do. The tears stood in her eyes, and she choked a little. She went back and forth between the two doors, and shook and pounded; she peeked around the corner of the curtain into the sitting-room. She could see Loretta's organ, with the music-book, and all the familiar furniture, but the room wore an utterly deserted air.

Finally, Ann Mary sat down on the front doorstep, after she had brushed off the snow a little. She had made up her mind to wait a little while, and see if the folks would not come home. She had on her red hood, and her grandmother's old plaid shawl. She pulled the shawl tightly around her, and muffled her face in it; it was extremely cold weather for sitting on a door-step. Just across the road was a low clump of birches; through and above the birches the sky showed red and clear where the sun was setting. Everything looked cold and bare and desolate to the little girl who was trying to keep Thanksgiving. Suddenly she heard a little cry, and Loretta's white cat came around the corner of the house.

"Kitty, kitty, kitty," called Ann Mary. She was very fond of Loretta's cat; she had none of her own.

The cat came close and brushed around Ann Mary so she took it up in her lap; and wrapped the shawl around it, and felt a little comforted.

She sat there on the door-step and held the cat until it was quite dusky, and she was very stiff with the cold. Then she put down the cat and prepared to go home. But she had not gone far along the road when she found out that the cat was following her. The little white creature floundered through the snow at her heels, and mewed constantly. Sometimes it darted ahead and waited until she came up, but it did not seem willing to be carried in her arms.

When Ann Mary reached her own house the lonesome look of it sent a chill all over her; she was afraid to go in. She made up her mind to go down to Sarah Bean's and ask whether she could not stay all night there.

So she kept on, and Loretta's white cat still followed her. There was no light in Sarah Bean's house. Ann Mary knocked and pounded, but it was of no use; the old woman had gone to bed, and she could not make her hear.

Ann Mary turned about and went home; the tears were running down her cold red cheeks. The cat mewed louder than ever. When she got home she took the cat up and carried it into the house. She determined to keep it for company, anyway. She was sure, now, that she would have to stay alone all night; the Adamses and Sarah Bean were the only neighbors, and it was so late now that she had no hope of her grandparents' return. Ann Mary was timid and nervous, but she had a vein of philosophy, and she generally grasped the situation with all the strength she had, when she became convinced that she must. She had laid her plans while walking home through the keen winter air, even as the tears were streaming over her cheeks, and she proceeded to carry them into execution. She gave Loretta's cat its

supper, and she ate a piece of mince-pie herself; then she fixed the kitchen and the sitting-
room fires, and locked up the house very thor-
oughly. Next, she took the cat and the lamp
and went into the dark bed-room and locked
the door; then she and the cat were as safe as
she knew how to make them. The dark bed-
room was in the very middle of the house, the
centre of a nest of rooms. It was small and
square, had no windows, and only one door.
It was a sort of fastness. Ann Mary made up
her mind that she would keep the lamp burning all night. She climbed into the big yellow-
posted bedstead, and the cat cuddled up to her
and purred.

Ann Mary lay in bed and stared at the white
satin scrolls on the wall-paper, and listened for
noises. She heard a great many, but they
were all mysterious and indefinable, till about
ten o'clock. Then she sat straight up in bed
and her heart beat fast. She certainly heard
sleigh-bells; the sound penetrated even to the
dark bedroom. Then came a jarring pounding
on the side door. Ann Mary got up, unfas-
tened the bedroom door, took the lamp, and
stepped out into the sitting-room. The pounding came again. "Ann Mary, Ann Mary!"
cried a voice. It was her granmother's.

"I'm comin', I'm comin', grandma!" shouted
Ann Mary. She had never felt so happy in
her life. She pushed back the bolt of the side

door with trembling haste. There stood her
grandmother all muffled up, with a shawl over
her head; and out in the yard were her grandfather and another man, with a horse and
sleigh. The men were turning the sleigh
around.

"Put the lamp in the window, Ann Mary,"
called Mr. Little, and Ann Mary obeyed. Her
grandmother sank into a chair. "I'm jest
about tuckered out," she groaned. "If I don't
ketch my death with this day's work, I'm lucky.
There ain't any more feelin' in my feet than as
if they were lumps of stone."

Ann Mary stood at her grandmother's elbow,
and her face was all beaming. "I thought you
weren't coming," said she.

"Well, I shouldn't have come a step to-
night, if it hadn't been for you — and the cow,"
said her grandmother, in an indignant voice.
"I was kind of uneasy about you, an' we knew
the cow wouldn't be milked unless you got Mr.
Adams to come over."

"Was Aunt Betsey very sick?" inquired
Ann Mary.

Her grandmother gave her head a toss.
"Sick! No, there wa'n't a thing the matter
with her, except she ate some sassage-meat, an'
had a little faint turn. Lizz was scart to death,
the way she always is. She didn't act as if she
knew whether her head was on, all the time
we were there. She didn't act as if she knew

'twas Thanksgivin' Day; an' she didn't have no turkey that I could see. Aunt Betsey bein' sick seemed to put everythin' out of her head. I never saw such a nervous thing as she is. I was all out of patience when I got there. Betsey didn't seem to be very bad off, an' there we'd hurried enough to break our necks. We didn't dare to drive around to Sarah Bean's to let you know about it, for we was afraid we'd miss the train. We jest got in with the man that brought the word, an' he driv as fast as he could over to the village, an' then we lost the train, an' had to sit there in the depot two mortal hours. An' now we've come fourteen mile' in an open sleigh. The man that lives next door to Betsey said he'd bring us home, an' I thought we'd better come. He's goin' over to the village to-night; he's got folks there. I told him he'd a' good deal better stay here, but he won't. He's as deaf as an adder, an' you can't make him hear anythin', anyway. We ain't spoke a word all the way home. Where's Loretty? She came over to stay with you, didn't she?"

Ann Mary explained that Loretta was not at home.

"That's queer, seems to me, Thanksgivin' Day," said her grandmother. "Massy sakes, what cat's that. She came out of the settin'-room!"

Ann Mary explained about Loretta's cat.

Then she burst forth with the question that had
been uppermost in her mind ever since her
grandmother came in. "Grandma," said she,
"what did you do with the turkey and the
plum-pudding?"

"What?"

"What did you do with the turkey and the
plum-pudding?"

"The turkey an' the plum-pudding?"

"Yes; I couldn't find 'em anywhere."

Mrs. Little, who had removed her wraps, and
was crouching over the kitchen stove with her
feet in the oven, looked at Ann Mary with a
dazed expression.

"I dunno what you mean, child," said she.

Mr. Little had helped the man with the sleigh
to start, and had now come in. He was pulling off his boots.

"Don't you remember, mother," said he,
"how you run back in the house, an' said you
was goin' to set that turkey an' plum-pudding
away, for you was afraid to leave 'em settin'
right out in plain sight on the table, for fear
that somebody might come in?"

"Yes; I do remember," said Mrs. Little. "I
thought they looked 'most too temptin'. I set
'em in the pantry. I thought Ann Mary could
get 'em when she came in."

"They ain't in the pantry," said Ann Mary.

Her grandmother arose and went into the
pantry with a masterful air. "Ain't in the

pantry?" she repeated. "I don't s'pose you more'n gave one look."

Ann Mary followed her grandmother. She fairly expected to see the turkey and pudding before her eyes on the shelf and to admit that she had been mistaken. Mr. Little also followed, and they all stood in the pantry and looked about.

"I guess they ain't here, mother," said Mr. Little. "Can't you think where you set 'em?"

The old woman took up the lamp and stepped out of the pantry with dignity. "I've set 'em somewhere," said she, in a curt voice, "an' I'll find 'em in the mornin'. You don't want any turkey or plum-pudding, to-night, neither of you!"

But Mrs. Little did not find the turkey and the plum-pudding in the morning. Some days went by, and their whereabouts was as much a mystery as ever. Mrs. Little could not remember where she had put them; but it had been in some secure hiding-place, since her own wit which had placed them there could not find it out. She was so mortified and worried over it that she was nearly ill. She tried to propound the theory, and believe in it herself, that she had really set the turkey and the pudding in the pantry, and that they had been stolen; but she was too honest. "I've heerd of folks puttin' things in such safe places that they couldn't find 'em, before now," said she; "but

I never heerd of losin' a turkey an' a plum-pudding that way. I dunno but I'm losin' what little wits I ever did have." She went about with a humble and resentful air. She promised Ann Mary that she would cook another turkey and pudding the first of the week, if the missing ones were not found.

Sunday came and they were not discovered. It was a pleasant day, and the Littles went to the village church. Ann Mary looked over across the church after they were seated and saw Loretta, with the pretty brown frizzes over her forehead, sitting between her father and mother, and she wondered when Loretta had come home.

The choir sang and the minister prayed. Suddenly Ann Mary saw him, standing there in the pulpit, unfold a paper. Then *the minister began to read the Thanksgiving Proclamation*. Ann Mary cast one queer glance at her grandmother, who returned it with one of inexpressible dignity and severity.

As soon as meeting was done, her grandmother clutched her by the arm. "Don't you say a word about it to anybody," she whispered. "You mind!"

When they were in the sleigh going home she charged her husband. "You mind, you keep still, father," said she. "It'll be town-talk if you don't."

The old man chuckled. "Don't you know,

I said once that I had kind of an idee that Thanksgivin' were'nt quite so early, and you shut me up, mother," he remarked. He looked good-naturedly malicious.

"Well, I dunno as it's anything so very queer," said Mrs. Little. "It comes a whole week later than it did last year, and I s'posed we'd missed hearin' the proclamation."

The next day a letter arrived saying that Lucy and her father and mother were coming to spend Thanksgiving. "I feel jest about beat," Mrs. Little said, when she read the letter.

Really, she did feel about at her wit's end. The turkey and pudding were not yet found, and she had made up her mind that she would not dare wait much longer without providing more. She knew that another turkey must be procured, at all events. However, she waited until the last minute Wednesday afternoon, then she went to work mixing a pudding. Mr. Little had gone to the store for the turkey. "Sam White was over there, an' he said he thought we was goin' right into turkeys this year," he reported when he got home.

That night the guests arrived. Thanksgiving morning Lucy and Ann Mary and their grandfather and Lucy's father and mother were all going to meeting. Mrs. Little was to stay at home and cook the dinner.

Thanksgiving morning Mr. Little made a fire in the best parlor air-tight stove, and just be-

fore they started for meeting Lucy and Ann
Mary were in the room. Lucy, in the big rock-
ing-chair that was opposite the sofa, was rocking to and fro and talking. Ann Mary sat
near the window. Each of the little girls had
on her coat and hat.

Suddenly Lucy stopped rocking and looked
intently over towards the sofa.

"What you lookin' at, Lucy?" asked Ann
Mary, curiously.

Lucy still looked. "Why — I was wondering what was under that sofa," said she, slowly.
Then she turned to Ann Mary, and her face
was quite pale and startled — she had heard
the turkey and pudding story. "Oh, Ann
Mary, it does look — like — oh —"

Both little girls rushed to the sofa, and
threw themselves on the floor. "Oh, oh, oh!"
they shrieked. "Grandma — mother! Come
quick, come quick!"

When the others came in, there sat Ann
Mary and Lucy on the floor, and between them
were the turkey and the plum-pudding, each
carefully covered with a snow-white napkin.

Mrs. Little was quite pale and trembling.
"I remember now," said she, faintly, "I run in
here with 'em."

She was so overcome that the others tried to
take it quietly and not to laugh much. But
every little while, after Lucy and Ann Mary
were seated in church, they would look at each

other and have to put their handkerchiefs in their faces. However, Ann Mary tried hard to listen to the sermon, and to behave well. In the depths of her childish heart she felt grateful and happy. There, by her side, sat her dear Lucy, whose sweet little face peeped out from a furry winter hat. Just across the aisle was Loretta, who was coming in the evening, and then they would pop corn and make nut-candy. At home there was the beautiful new turkey and unlimited pudding and good cheer, and all disappointment and mystery were done away with.

Ann Mary felt as if all her troubles would be followed by thanksgivings.

* * * *Wilkin.*

SELECTION

J. G. WHITTIER

Heap high the farmer's wintry hoard!
　Heap high the golden corn!
No richer gift has Autumn poured
　From out her lavish horn.

Let other lands exulting glean
　The apple from the pine,
The orange from its glossy green,
　The cluster from the vine.

* * * * * * *

But let the good old corn adorn
   The hills our fathers trod;
Still let us, for His golden corn,
   Send up our thanks to God.

THE TWILIGHT OF THANKSGIVING

WILLIAM D. KELLY

The day has lengthened into eve,
   And over all the meadows
The twilight's silent shuttles weave
   Their sombre web of shadows;
With northern lights the cloudless skies
   Are faintly phosphorescent,
And just above yon wooded rise
   The new moon shows her crescent.

Before the evening lamps are lit,
   While day and night commingle,
The sire and matron come and sit
   Beside the cozy ingle;
And softly speak of the delight
   Within their bosoms swelling,
Because beneath their roof to-night
   Their dear ones all are dwelling.

And when around the cheerful blaze
   The young folks take their places,
What blissful dreams of other days
   Light up their aged faces!

The past returns with all its joys,
  And they again are living
The years in which, as girls and boys,
  Their children kept Thanksgiving.

The stalwart son recalls the time
  When, urged to the endeavor,
He tried the well-greased pole to climb,
  And failed of fame forever.
The daughter tells of her emprise
  When, as a new beginner,
She helped her mother make the pies
  For the Thanksgiving dinner.

And thus with laugh and jest and song,
  And tender recollections,
Love speeds the happy hours along,
  And fosters fond affections;
While Fancy, listening to the mirth,
  And dreaming pleasant fictions,
Imagines through the winds on earth
  That heaven breathes benedictions.

POLLY'S THANKSGIVING

A. C. STODDARD

Such a funny little roly-poly Polly as she was, with her big china-blue eyes that were forever seeing something to wonder about, and her round, red cheeks that always grew redder when anybody spoke to her, and her crinkly flaxen hair that never would stay in place. Such a queer little dumpling of a Polly!

All the same, she liked nice things to eat as well as any one could, and when, once upon a time, somebody gave her the measles just in season for Thanksgiving Day, she felt dreadfully about it, and cried as hard as she knew how because she couldn't have any turkey, nor pudding, nor mince-pie for dinner — nothing at all but oatmeal gruel.

But crying didn't help the measles a mite, as of course Polly knew it wouldn't, but she couldn't have helped crying if she wanted to, and she didn't want to.

" 'Most anybody'd cried, I wouldn't wonder," she said, a day or two after, when the measles had begun to go away again, "not to have a mite of any Thanksgiving for dinner,

not any pie, not any cranb'ry sauce, not any —
O de-ar!"

"Well, well," said Polly's mother, laughing,
"I guess we'll have to have another Thanksgiving Day right off."

"Oh! can we?" cried Polly, brightening up.

"Not without the governor says so," answered her father, with a twinkle. "The governor makes Thanksgiving Days, Polyanthus."

"Where does he live?" asked Polly, with
an earnestness that was funny. Everybody
laughed.

"At the capital," said Polly's Uncle Ben
Davis. "Do you know where that is?"

"I guess I do," said Polly, and she asked no
more questions.

But what do you guess this funny Polly did?
By and by, when she felt quite herself again,
she borrowed pencil and paper and shut herself
up in her own little room and wrote a letter
that looked a little queer, 'tis true, but still made
her wishes known.

"DeRe MisTeR Guvner will yOu PLeAse
Make AnoTHeR Thanksgiving DAy be
caws I haD THE MEESLES the LAst One.
"Polly Pinkham."

Then she folded the letter and put it in an
envelope, with one of her chromo cards, and
sealed it, and took two cents out of her bank

for the postage and ran away to the post-office as fast as she could run.

Mr. Willey kept the post-office, and if he himself had been behind the glass boxes that day, I don't believe Polly's letter ever would have gone out of Tinkerville. But Mr. Willey's niece was there. She read the address on the envelope Polly handed in, and her eyes danced. It looked so funny:

" Mister GuvNER, at the CAPITLE."

One or two questions brought out the whole story.

" The governor shall have your letter, Polly," roguish Miss Molly said, with a laugh, as she stamped it and wrote the postmark plain as plain could be.

And so he did. For, not quite a week later, a letter came in the mail to Polly — a great, white letter with a picture in one corner that made Polly's father open his eyes.

" Why, it's the State's arms," said he. " What under the sun —"

But I think he suspected. Oh! how red Polly's cheeks were, and how her small fingers trembled when she tore open her letter. It was printed so that she could read it herself, all but the long words.

" Dear Miss Polly : — Your letter received. I am very sorry you were so ill as not to be able to eat any Thanksgiving dinner. It was quite too bad. I hereby appoint a special Thanksgiving Day for you — next Thursday, December 9th — which I trust may be kept with due form.   " Your friend and well-wisher,

" Andrew Colburn."

" Oh! oh! oh!" cried Polly, hopping on one foot, " will you mother? O mother! will you? I wrote to him myself. Oh! I'm so glad."

" Did you ever!" cried Polly's mother. " Why, Polly Pinkham!" But Polly's father slapped his knee and laughed.

" Good for Governor Colburn! I'll vote for him as long as he wants a vote. And Polly shall have a special Thanksgiving worth telling of, so she shall."

And so she did have, the very best she ever remembered.

THANKSGIVING DAY

IN THE OLD CHURCH TOWER

THOMAS BAILEY ALDRICH

In the old church tower
  Hangs the bell;
And above it on the vane,
In the sunshine and the rain,

Cut in gold, St. Peter stands,
With the keys in his claspt hands,
 And all is well.

In the old church tower
 Hangs the bell;
You can hear its great heart beat,
Ah, so loud and wild and sweet,
As the parson says a prayer
Over wedded lovers there,
 And all is well.

In the old church tower
 Hangs the bell;
Deep and solemn, hark! again,
Ah, what passion and what pain!
With her hands upon her breast,
Some poor soul has gone to rest
 Where all is well.

In the old church tower
 Hangs the bell;
An old friend that seems to know
All our joy and all our woe;
It is glad when we are wed,
It is sad when we are dead,
 And all is well.

THANKSGIVING DAY

HENRY ALFORD

Come, ye thankful people, come,
Raise the song of Harvest-home!
All is safely gathered in,
Ere the winter storms begin;
God, our Maker, doth provide
For our wants to be supplied;
Come to God's own temple, come;
Raise the song of Harvest-home!

What is earth but God's own field,
Fruit unto his praise to yield?
Wheat and tares therein are sown,
Unto joy or sorrow grown;
Ripening with a wondrous power,
Till the final Harvest-hour:
Grant, O Lord of life, that we
Holy grain and pure may be.

Come, then, Lord of Mercy, come,
Bid us sing the Harvest-home!
Let thy saints be gathered in!
Free from sorrow, free from sin;
All upon the golden floor
Praising thee forevermore;
Come, with thousand angels, come;
Bid us sing thy Harvest-home.

AN OLD TIME THANKSGIVING

HELEN EVERTSON SMITH

The following account of a Thanksgiving dinner in 1779 is given in a letter of Juliana Smith's, copied by her into her diary — a praiseworthy practice not uncommon when letters were written with care and might easily be lost in transmission. This letter was addressed to its writer's "Dear Cousin Betsey." Who the latter may have been I do not know, but presume that she was a daughter of the Rev. C. M. Smith's elder brother Dan.

After the usual number of apologies for delay in writing, Juliana proceeds:

"When Thanksgiving Day was approaching our dear Grandmother Smith (*née* Jerusha Mather, great-granddaughter of the Rev. Richard Mather of Dorchester, Massachusetts), who is sometimes a little desponding of Spirit as you well know, did her best to persuade us that it would be better to make it a Day of Fasting & Prayer in view of the *Wickedness of our Friends &c. the Vileness of our Enemies,* I am sure you can hear Grandmother say that

and see her shake her cap border. But indeed
there was some occasion for her remarks, for
our resistance to an *unjust Authority* has cost
our beautiful Coast Towns very dear the last
year & all of us have had much to suffer.
But my dear Father brought her to a more
proper frame of Mind, so that by the time the
Day came she was ready to enjoy it almost as
well as Grandmother Worthington did, & she,
you will remember, always sees the bright side.
In the mean while we had all of us been working hard to get all things in readiness to do
honour to the Day.

"This year it was Uncle Simeon's turn to
have the dinner at his house, but of course we
all helped them as they help us when it is our
turn, & there is always enough for us all to
do. All the baking of pies & cakes was done
at our house & we had the big oven heated
& filled twice each day for three days before
it was all done, & *everything was* GOOD,
though we did have to do without some things
that ought to be used. Neither Love nor
(paper) Money could buy Raisins, but our
good red cherries dried without the pits, did
almost as well & happily Uncle Simeon still
had some spices in store. The tables were set
in the Dining Hall and even that big room
had no space to spare when we were all seated.
The Servants had enough ado to get around
the Tables & serve us all without over-setting

things. There were our two Grandmothers
side by side. They are always handsome old
Ladies, but now, many thought, they were
handsomer than ever, & happy they were to look
around upon so many of their descendants.
Uncle & Aunt Simeon presides at one Table, &
Father & Mother at the other. Besides us five
boys & girls there were two of the Gales &
three Elmers, besides James Browne & Ephraim
Cowles. (Five of the last-named seven, were
orphans taught and in all ways provided for by
Parson & Mrs. Smith.) We had them at our
table because they could be best *supervised*
there. Most of the students had gone to their
own homes for the weeks, but Mr. Skiff and
Mr. ——, (name illegible) were too far away
from their homes. They sat at Uncle Simeon's table & so did Uncle Paul and his family,
five of them in all, & Cousins Phin & Poll
(probably Phineas and Apollos Smith, sons of
Dan). Then there were six of the Livingston
family next door. They had never seen a
Thanksgiving Dinner before, having been used
to keep Christmas Day instead, as is the wont
in New York & Province. Then there were
four Old Ladies who have no longer Homes or
Children of their own & so came to us. They
were invited by my Mother, but Uncle and
Aunt Simeon wished it so.

"Of course we could have no Roast Beef.
None of us have tasted Beef this three years

back as it all must go to the Army, & too
little they get, poor fellows. But, Nayquitty-
maw's Hunters were able to get us a fine
red Deer, so that we had a good haunch of
Venisson on each Table. These were balanced
by huge Chines of Roast Pork at the other
ends of the Tables. Then there was on one
a big Roast Turkey & on the other a Goose,
& two big Pigeon Pasties. Then there was
an abundance of good Vegetables of all the
old Sorts & one which I do not believe you have
yet seen. Uncle Simeon had imported the
Seede from England just before the War began & only this Year was there enough for
Table use. It is called Sellery & you eat it
without cooking. It is very good served with
meats. Next year Uncle Simeon says he will
be able to raise enough to give us all some.
It has to be taken up, roots & all & buried in
earth in the cellar through the winter & only
pulling up some when you want it to use.

"Our Mince Pies were good although we
had to use dried Cherries as I told you, & the
meat was shoulder of Venisson, instead of
Beef. The Pumpkin Pies, Apple Tarts & big
Indian Puddings lacked for nothing save *Appetite* by the time we had got round to them.

"Of course we had no Wine. Uncle Simeon
has still a cask or two, but it must all be
saved for the sick, & indeed, for those who are
well, good Cider is a sufficient Substitute.

There was no Plumb Pudding, but a boiled
Suet Pudding, stirred thick with dried Plumbs
& Cherries, was called by the old Name & answered the purpose. All the other spice had
been used in the Mince Pies, so for this Pudding we used a jar of West India preserved
Ginger which chanced to be left of the last ship-
ment which Uncle Simeon had from there, we
chopped the Ginger small and stirred it through
with the Plumbs and Cherries. It was *extraordinary* goods. The Day was bitter cold &
when we got home from Meeting, which Father
did not keep over long by reason of the cold,
we were glad eno' of the fire in Uncle's Dining
Hall, but by the time the dinner was one-half
over those of us who were on the fire side of
one Table was forced to get up & carry our
plates with us around to the far side of the
other Table, while those who had sat there
were as glad to bring their plates around to
the fire side to get warm. All but the Old
Ladies who had a screen put behind their
chairs."

Here it may be allowed to break in upon
Juliana's narrative to explain that the hall in
which this dinner was laid, now long used as a
kitchen, is a room about thirty feet long from
north to south and twenty-two feet wide. A
glazed door and a window open upon piazzas
from each end. On the western side a broadly

hospitable door opens into the staircase hall of the main building, while in the dining-room itself another flight of stairs ascended from the same side to the wing's chambers. On the eastern side is the immense chimney, where once yawned a fireplace that "would comfortably hold a full sled load of eight foot logs." With such a fire it is no wonder that the guests seated near it were glad to exchange places with the others, who — probably half freezing — were on the other side of the room. When I was about seven or eight years old the heavy ceiling beams, darkened with age and smoke, were hidden away from view by a plaster ceiling. I pleaded in vain for the "pretty brown beams" to be left in sight, but my grandmother was inflexible, and no doubt, in the interest of comfort for her servants, she was quite right to close the drafty fireplace and lower the lofty ceiling. Nevertheless it was a pity, and I have never ceased to regret it.

"Uncle Simeon," proceeds Juliana, "was in his best mood, and you know how good that is! He kept both Tables in a roar of laughter with his droll stories of the days when he was studying medicine in Edinborough, & afterwards he & Father & Uncle Paul joined in singing Hymns & Ballads. You know how fine their voices go together. Then we all sang a Hymn and afterwards my dear Father led us in prayer, remembering all Absent Friends before the Throne of Grace, & much I wished that my dear Betsey was here as one of us, as she has been of yore.

" We did not rise from the Table until it was quite dark, & then when the dishes had been cleared away we all got round the fire as close as we could, & cracked nuts, & sang songs & told stories. At least some told & others listened. *You know nobody* can exceed the two Grandmothers at telling tales of all the things they have seen themselves, & repeating those of the early years in New England, & even some in the Old England, which they had heard in their youth from their Elders. My Father says it is a goodly custom to hand down all worthy deeds & traditions from Father to Son, as the Israelites were commanded to do about the Passover & as the Indians here have always done, because the Word that is spoken is remembered longer than the one that is written . . . Brother Jack, who did not reach here until late on Wednesday though he had left College very early on Monday Morning & rode with all due diligence considering the snow, brought an orange to each of the Grand-Mothers, but Alas! they were frozen in his saddle bags. We soaked the frost out in cold water, but I guess they wasn't as good as they should have been?"

* * *

III

THE SPIRIT OF THANKS-GIVING

THE THANKSGIVING GUEST

LOUISE CHANDLER MOULTON

"Not going to make any thanksgiving this year?"

Deacon Comstock's face expressed the utmost astonishment of which it was capable. He had come in from doing his morning "chores," and found his wife sitting down with her knitting, on this — the day before Thanksgiving — the day which should, according to all precedent, have been the busiest in the year.

"Want any help, mother?" he had said cheerfully. "Anything I can do for you before I go out to kill the turkey?"

And then came a sudden burst of tears that quite startled him; for Mrs. Comstock was not one of the crying kind of women, and she said, amid her sobs, that she wasn't going to make any thanksgiving this year — why should she? — what had she to be thankful for?

Deacon Comstock understood her well enough, for all the astonishment in his face and his voice. God's hand had been laid upon them this year, heavily. Three years before, their only son — a reckless, roistering lad, in whom there was less of actual harm than of merry mischief and impatience of restraint — had run away from his sober, Puritanical home, and gone to sea. They had never heard of him since. They knew not whether the deep sea held him or under what strange skies he sailed, — on what far-off shores he roamed. This blow had been hard to bear; but Deacon John Comstock and his wife called themselves Christians, and they tried to submit their hearts in patience. And when thanksgiving time came, and they missed merry Jack so sorely, his sister, their only daughter, had brought home, to comfort them in Jack's stead, her first baby,— a little rosy boy, just old enough to laugh up in their faces, and hold out chubby arms to go from one to the other.

Two more thanksgiving times had come and gone since then, and that child had been their consolation. His baby kisses had soothed away their heartache. With him and his father and mother to welcome, there had been something for which to make thanksgiving.

But neither baby Joe nor his fair young mother would ever again come smiling home. One of those summer days when earth and sky seem to meet and mingle, the gates of heaven had been left ajar, and a voice had called to child and mother. There had been a few days of terrible illness,— the pang with which soul and body had parted,— and then in the sum-

mer twilight the boy had laid his golden head
on his mother's breast, and her arms had folded
round him; and so the watchers coming in had
found them,— lying as if asleep, with the wonderful death-smile frozen upon their lips,—
sweet lips that would never stir more.

They had been brought back to the old homestead, and buried in one grave; and then
Martha's husband had gone away to seek solace among strange scenes. He was young and
strong, and for him time might bring comfort;
but a bitterer woe, for which change of scene
would have offered no balm, settled down upon
the stricken parents. The mother, especially,
mourned night and day with an agony which
would not be comforted. She said nothing;
but you could read her mutinous misery in the
thin, wasting form, the eyes which solitary
weeping had dimmed, and the hair turning
white so fast. Now that at last she had begun
to speak, words, bitter, rebellious words came
hotly.

"God has not been merciful, John. To
thank Him would be a mockery. I lost Jack,
and I bore it, and thought that in some unknown way it must be meant for good. But I
had Martha then, and little Joe, and now they,
too, are gone. Shall I make a feast for the
dead to eat? Whom have we left among the
living?"

"And yet, mother, let us make the feast, and

it may be that the guests will come. For five
and twenty years we have not failed to keep
this festival together. Let us not pass it over
now with thankless hearts. I, too, have
mourned for our children,— for those gone before us to heaven and glory, and for the wanderer whose fate we do not know. But I see
the Father's mercy yet, for He has left me you,
my dearest."

He stopped, and his hand rested on his wife's
shoulder with a tender touch. His words had
pierced through her sullen sorrow, her numb
despair, right to the core of her heart. His
dearest! Was not he that to her, also; and,
with him by her side, had she dared to say she
had nothing for which to be thankful? What
if he, too, had been taken? She looked at him
with eyes in whose loving depths he never
missed their girlish brightness, and said, with
a new sweetness in her quivering voice,—

"I have sinned, John. God *has* been merciful in sparing you. I have yet something for
which to keep thanksgiving. We will make
our feast as usual. If no guests come, we can
send of our abundance to the poor and the
needy, and we will partake together of Heav-
en's bounty with thankful hearts — we two —
as we used to do in those first years before the
children came."

All the rest of that day there was no lack of
stir and bustle in Deacon Comstock's house.

The mistress omitted nothing of the usual thanksgiving preparations. She made the pies, the plum-pudding, the delicate cakes and jellies, — every trifle that Jack or Martha had loved she took pleasure in preparing, as a sort of memorial offering. So busied, the day, which she had meant to make one of gloomy, selfish, thankless indulgence in her sorrow, passed quickly; and at night, tired though she was, her face wore a look at once brighter and more peaceful than her husband had seen on it since Martha and Martha's child had gone to sleep in the summer twilight.

Through the evening they sat and talked together,— peaceful, tender talk about the dead, and about the absent. Especially they spoke of Jack, of his merry, boyish ways, of his loving heart, of his courage and his truth. All that was noblest in him seemed to live again in their memories. They forgot how wilful, and obstinate, and hard to rule he was, and only remembered him at his best.

" My mind misgives me often, mother, lest we were too hard on the boy," the deacon said, at last. " I think we drew the reins too tight, and his mettle was too high to stand it. And now no one knows what his fate will be ! "

" Yes, God knows," the wife answered softly. Since morning, convinced anew of God's mercy to herself, her faith seemed somehow to have grown. " God is as near to him, John, as to us,— on the sea as well as on the land. We shall see the boy again,— if not here, there, where there is no sea. It is borne in upon my mind that the Lord will hear our prayers, and that when we walk in His heaven we shall not miss the face of our boy."

And then hand in hand they knelt and prayed for their wanderer,— for all wanderers,— for all sorrow-stricken and lonely souls,— for all those who grope in the darkness of this world, — prayed that the celestial morning might break for them by-and-by, and the tired feet rest safely where wait the many mansions.

The snow had begun falling with the twilight. The rambling country village was still. Under every home-roof the loved ones were gathered in, sheltered from storm, and cold, and care,— waiting for the morrow. There seemed something ominous in the very stillness to a traveller who walked along the highway. He had stopped at a railroad station two miles off, whither he had come in a late train, and he was now making his way on foot, through the softly falling snow, over paths which seemed to be familiar to him. It made him think of cerements folded above the dead,— this white, still-falling snow which was covering the cold, frozen shape of hills and valleys. A fear stole into his heart and chilled the blood in his veins,— a superstitious fear, perhaps, born of the night stillness, the gleaming snow, the darkness through which all objects loomed ghostly and uncertain as phantoms. He turned aside from the highway, and walked rapidly through a lane into a little country graveyard, and on among the graves, until he reached the farthest corner, and stood under the shade of a great, heavily drooping willow, in a lot set apart from the rest by an iron railing.

Then he stood and counted the grave-stones, — grandfather, grandmother, two uncles, the tiny slab with his baby sister's name, the sister whom he could just remember as a blue-eyed wonder, with golden curls and lips as bright as red berries,— all those he knew; but whose was that other stone, which was not there when last he stood under that willow? He brushed away the snow with his hand, and felt for the inscription which it was too dark to see. But his fingers were almost stiffened with the cold, and he could only be sure of the first letter, a capital M. His fears sprang into the stature of convictions,— it was the initial letter of his mother's name. This, then, was the work which these three years had wrought,— the home he was coming to was one where no mother's face would smile, no mother's voice would welcome him. And if his going away had killed *her*, what hope was there that his father would ever forgive him? Might he not as well go back in the night and the storm, and carry his sor-row with him,— vanish, as he had come, in the darkness, making no sign? For a moment, standing irresolute among those graves, under that willow, he argued the question with himself; and then it seemed to him that a voice he used to know and love called him, as one might call a lost child through the darkness,—

"Come home, boy, come home!"

He hesitated no longer, but walked on swiftly through the falling snow, until he stood before Deacon John Comstock's door, and lifted the ponderous knocker with a hand that trembled despite the brave courage of his young manhood. He drew his soft hat close over his eyes, and wrapped his coat round him, with its collar turned up, so that only a straight nose and a bit of brown beard were in sight when the deacon opened the door.

"It is storming," he said. "Can you give me shelter?"

It was not the boyish voice which used to ring so merrily in Martha Comstock's ears,— it was fuller, deeper than that other voice, and less smooth,— but there was something in it which made her heart beat chokingly. The stranger crossed the threshold, and the light fell on the little of his face that was in sight. She had kissed a beardless boy the last time she bade merry Jack good-night; but no change of voice, no bronze or beard deceived the mother's heart.

"Our Father has sent the guest!" she cried;

"Oh, John, He has sent the guest!" as she sprang forward and took her own boy, snow and all, into her close, trembling arms. "My boy! my own boy Jack!" murmured into the wanderer's ears the fond, fond voice he had longed to hear through so many nights, tossing on stormy seas, with only a plank between him and eternity. He was indeed at home.

HARVEST HYMN

JOHN G. WHITTIER

Once more the liberal year laughs out
   O'er richer stores than gems of gold;
Once more with harvest song and shout
   Is nature's boldest triumph told.

Our common mother rests and sings
   Like Ruth among her garnered sheaves;
Her lap is full of goodly things,
   Her brow is bright with autumn leaves.

Oh, favors old, yet ever new;
   Oh, blessings with the sunshine sent!
The bounty overruns our due,
   The fullness shames our discontent.

We shut our eyes, the bowers bloom on;
   We murmur, but the corn ears fill;

We choose the shadow, but the sun
  That casts it shines behind us still,

And gives us, with our rugged soil,
  The power to make it Eden fair,
And richer fruits to crown our toil,
  Than summer-wedded islands bear.

Who murmurs at his lot today?
  Who scorns his native fruit and bloom,
Or sighs for dainties far away,
  Besides the bounteous board of home?

Thank heaven, instead, that freedom's arm
  Can change a rocky soil to gold;
That brave and generous lives can warm
  A clime with northern ices cold.

And by these altars wreathed with flowers,
  And fields with fruits awake again
Thanksgiving for the golden hours,
  The earlier and the latter rain.

THANKSGIVING

F. R. HAVERGAL

Thanks be to God! to whom earth owes
  Sunshine and breeze,
The heath-clad hill, the vale's repose,
  Streamlet and seas,

The snowdrop and the summer rose,
  The many-voiced trees,

Thanks for the darkness that reveals
  Night's starry dower;
And for the sable cloud that heals
  Each fevered flower;
And for the rushing storm that peals
  Our weakness and Thy power.

Thanks for the sweetly-lingering might
  In music's tone;
For paths of knowledge, whose calm light
  Is all thine own;
For thoughts that at the Infinite
  Fold their bright wings alone.

Yet thanks that silence oft may flow
  In dewlike store;
Thanks for the mysteries that show
  How small our lore;
Thanks that we here so little know
  And trust Thee all the more!

Thanks for the gladness that entwines
  Our path below;
Each sunrise that incarnadines
  The cold, still snow;
Thanks for the light of love which shines
  With brightest earthly glow.

Thanks for Thine own thrice-blessed Word,
   And Sabbath rest;
Thanks for the hope of glory stored
   In mansions blest;
Thanks for the Spirit's comfort poured
   Into the trembling breast.

Thanks, more thanks, to Him ascend,
   Who died to win
Our life, and every trophy rend
   From Death and Sin;
Till, when the thanks of earth shall end,
   The thanks of Heaven begin.

TWO FESTIVALS

LUCY LARCOM

Thanksgiving stirs her ruddy fire;
   The glow illuminates November:
She sees new glimmerings of desire
   Flash up from every fading ember.
The corn is stored, and heaped the board;
   The matron Day, her comforts summing,
Hears, through her best, a better word,—
   The merry shout of " Christmas coming ! "

The fires of two home-festivals
   Light up the frosty air together;

Thanksgiving unto Christmas calls,
    " Shake hands across this keen, cold
        weather!
We both are here to bring good cheer;
    Each has a heart-glow for the other;
The chill of our New England year
    Welcomes your warmth, my Old-World
        brother.

" My Pilgrims thought your wassail rude,
    Your Yule-flames a barbaric splendor;
Your gay old English game eschewed,
    Their graver gratitude to render
For hardship past, for peace at last.
    Now, with a larger comprehending,
We catch your cheerful meaning vast,
    That gives the year a blessed ending."

*   *   *   *   *   *   *   *

So Christmas and Thanksgiving clasp
    Their hands, and brightly bridge Decem-
        ber.
Close met within that heart-felt grasp,
    All friends One Friend of all remember.
Two feast-fires glow across the snow:
    Dead voices answer to the living,
As home to meet our own we go;
    ' Praise God for Christmas and Thanks-
        giving!"

JOHN INGLEFIELD'S THANKSGIVING

NATHANIEL HAWTHORNE

On the evening of Thanksgiving Day, John
Inglefield, the blacksmith, sat in his elbow-
chair, among those who had been keeping
festival at his board. Being the central figure
of the domestic circle, the fire threw its strong-
est light on his massive and sturdy frame, red-
dening his rough visage, so that it looked like
the head of an iron statue, all aglow, from his
own forge, and with its features rudely fash-
ioned on his own anvil. At John Inglefield's
right hand was an empty chair. The other
places round the hearth were filled by the members of the family, who all sat quietly, while,
with a semblance of fantastic merriment, their
shadows danced on the wall behind them. One
of the group was John Inglefield's son, who had
been bred at college, and was now a student of
theology at Andover. There was also a daughter of sixteen, whom nobody could look at without thinking of a rosebud almost blossomed.
The only other person at the fireside was
Robert Moore, formerly an apprentice of the
blacksmith, but now his journeyman, and who

seemed more like an own son of John Inglefield than did the pale and slender student.

Only these four had kept New England's
festival beneath that roof. The vacant chair at
John Inglefield's right hand was in memory of
his wife, whom death had snatched from him
since the previous Thanksgiving. With a feeling that few would have looked for in his rough
nature, the bereaved husband had himself set
the chair in its place next his own; and often
did his eye glance hitherward, as if he deemed
it possible that the cold grave might send back
its tenant to the cheerful fireside, at least for
that one evening. Thus did he cherish the
grief that was dear to him. But there was
another grief which he would fain have torn
from his heart; or, since that could never be,
have buried it too deep for others to behold,
or for his own remembrance. Within the past
year another member of his household had gone
from him, but not to the grave. Yet they kept
no vacant chair for her.

While John Inglefield and his family were
sitting round the hearth with the shadows danc-
ing behind them on the wall, the outer door
was opened, and a light footstep came along
the passage. The latch of the inner door was
lifted by some familiar hand, and a young girl
came in, wearing a cloak and hood, which she
took off and laid on the table beneath the look-
ing-glass. Then, after gazing a moment at

the fireside circle, she approached, and took
the seat at John Inglefield's right hand, as if
it had been reserved on purpose for her.

"Here I am, at last, father," said she. "You
ate your Thanksgiving dinner without me, but
I have come back to spend the evening with
you."

Yes, it was Prudence Inglefield. She wore
the same neat and maidenly attire which she
had been accustomed to put on when the household work was over for the day, and her hair
was parted from her brow, in the simple and
modest fashion that became her best of all.
If her cheek might otherwise have been pale,
yet the glow of the fire suffused it with a
healthful bloom. If she had spent the many
months of her absence in guilt and infamy, yet
they seemed to have left no traces on her gentle
aspect. She could not have looked less altered, had she merely stepped away from her
father's fireside for half an hour, and returned
while the blaze was quivering upwards from
the same brands that were burning at her de-
parture. And to John Inglefield she was the
very image of his buried wife, such as he remembered on the first Thanksgiving which
they had passed under their own roof. Therefore, though naturally a stern and rugged man,
he could not speak unkindly to his sinful child,
nor yet could he take her to his bosom.

"You are welcome home, Prudence," said

he, glancing sideways at her, and his voice
faltered. "Your mother would have rejoiced
to see you, but she has been gone from us
these four months."

"I know, father, I know it," replied Prudence, quickly. "And yet, when I first came
in, my eyes were so dazzled by the firelight
that she seemed to be sitting in this very
chair?"

By this time, the other members of the family
had begun to recover from their surprise, and
became sensible that it was no ghost from the
grave, nor vision of their vivid recollections,
but Prudence, her own self. Her brother was
the next that greeted her. He advanced and
held out his hand affectionately, as a brother
should; yet not entirely like a brother, for,
with all his kindness, he was still a clergyman
and speaking to a child of sin.

"Sister Prudence," said he, earnestly, "I rejoice that a merciful Providence hath turned
your steps homeward, in time for me to bid you
a last farewell. In a few weeks, sister, I am
to sail as a missionary to the far islands of
the Pacific. There is not one of these be-
loved faces that I shall ever hope to behold
again on this earth. Oh, may I see all of them
— yours and all — beyond the grave!"

A shadow flitted across the girl's countenance.

"The grave is very dark, brother," answered

she, withdrawing her hand somewhat hastily from his grasp. "You must look your last at me by the light of this fire."

While this was passing, the twin girl — the rosebud that had grown on the same stem with the castaway — stood gazing at her sister, longing to fling herself upon her bosom, so that the tendrils of their hearts might intertwine again. At first she was restrained by mingled grief and shame, and by a dread that Prudence was too much changed to respond to her affection, or that her own purity would be felt as a reproach by the lost one. But, as she listened to the familiar voice, while the face grew more and more familiar, she forgot everything save that Prudence had come back. Springing forward, she would have clasped her in a close embrace. At that very instant, however, Prudence started from her chair, and held out both her hands, with a warning gesture.

"No, Mary,— no, my sister," cried she, " do not you touch me. Your bosom must not be pressed to mine!"

Mary shuddered and stood still, for she felt that something darker than the grave was between Prudence and herself, though they seemed so near each other in the light of their father's hearth, where they had grown up together. Meanwhile Prudence threw her eyes around the room, in search of one who had not yet bidden her welcome. He had withdrawn from his seat by the fireside, and was standing near the door, with his face averted so that his features could be discerned only by the flickering shadow of the profile upon the wall. But Prudence called to him, in a cheerful and kindly tone:—

".Come, Robert," said she, " won't you shake hands with your old friend?"

Robert Moore held back for a moment, but affection struggled powerfully, and overcame his pride and resentment; he rushed towards Prudence, seized her hand, and pressed it to his bosom.

"There, there, Robert," said she, smiling sadly, as she withdrew her hand, "you must not give me too warm a welcome."

And now, having exchanged greetings with each member of the family, Prudence again seated herself in the chair at John Inglefield's right hand. She was naturally a girl of quick and tender sensibilities, gladsome in her general mood, but with a bewitching pathos interfused among her merriest words and deeds. It was remarked of her, too, that she had a faculty, even from childhood, of throwing her own feelings like a spell over her companions. Such as she had been in her days of innocence, so did she appear this evening. Her friends, in the surprise and bewilderment of her return, almost forgot that she had ever left them, or that she had forfeited any of her claims to their affection. In the morning, perhaps, they might have looked at her with altered eyes, but by the Thanksgiving fireside they felt only that their own Prudence had come back to them, and were thankful. John Inglefield's rough visage brightened with the glow of his heart, as it grew warm and merry within him; once or twice, even, he laughed till the room rang again, yet seemed startled by the echo of his own mirth. The brave young minister became as frolicsome as a schoolboy. Mary, too, the rosebud, forgot that her twin-blossom had ever been torn from the stem and trampled in the dust. And as for Robert Moore, he gazed at Prudence with the bashful earnestness of love new-born, while she, with sweet maiden coquetry, half smiled upon and half discouraged him.

In short, it was one of those intervals when sorrow vanishes in its own depth of shadow, and joy starts forth in transitory brightness. When the clock struck eight, Prudence poured out her father's customary draught of herb tea, which had been steeping by the fireside ever since twilight.

"God bless you, child," said John Inglefield, as he took the cup from her hand; "you have made your old father happy again. But we miss your mother sadly, Prudence, sadly. It seems as if she ought to be here now."

"Now, father, or never," replied Prudence.

It was now the hour for domestic worship. But while the family were making preparations for this duty, they suddenly perceived that Prudence had put on her cloak and hood, and was lifting the latch of the door.

"Prudence, Prudence! where are you going?" cried they all with one voice.

As Prudence passed out of the door, she turned towards them, and flung back her hand with a gesture of farewell. But her face was so changed that they hardly recognized it. Sin and evil passions glowed through its comeliness, and wrought a horrible deformity; a smile gleamed in her eyes, as of triumphant mockery, at their surprise and grief.

"Daughter," cried John Inglefield, between wrath and sorrow, "stay and be your father's blessing, or take his curse with you!"

For an instant Prudence lingered and looked back into the fire-lighted room, while her countenance wore almost the expression as if she were struggling with a fiend, who had power to seize his victim even within the hallowed precincts of her father's hearth. The fiend prevailed; and Prudence vanished into the outer darkness. When the family rushed to the door, they could see nothing, but heard the sound of wheels rattling over the frozen ground.

That same night, among the painted beauties at the theatre of a neighboring city, there was one whose dissolute mirth seemed inconsistent with any sympathy for pure affections, and for the joys and griefs which are hallowed by them. Yet this was Prudence Inglefield. Her visit to the Thanksgiving fireside was the realization of one of those waking dreams in which the guilty soul will sometimes stray back to its innocence. But Sin, alas! is careful of her bondslaves; they hear her voice, perhaps, at the holiest moment, and are constrained to go whither she summons them. The same dark power that drew Prudence Inglefield from her father's hearth — the same in its nature, though heightened then to a dread necessity — would snatch a guilty soul from the gate of heaven, and make its sin and its punishment alike eternal.

———

THE "LILY'S" THANKSGIVING

MRS. DAWSON M. PHELPS

It was always the time for a laugh, when the name
  Of Lily O'Brian was called;
You couldn't but smile at the humorous way,
  And the mock-serious tone it was drawled.

And she seemed like a pendulum swinging between,
  With a halt at the corner saloon,

The jail and police court; police court and jail,
  To the time of a sixty days' tune.

The next would be Thanksgiving Day, as
      again,
  She bade her jail comrades good-bye.
And stood at the door, as one leaving her home,
  With a tear in her whiskey-dulled eye.

And the matron had said, "It's a pity you'll
      miss
  Our Thanksgiving,"— midst peals of rude
      laughter,—
"But I'll save you a bit of the turkey and
      things,
  For you'll surely be here the day after."

"And it's kind that ye are," answered Lily
      O'Brian,
  "And thruly Oi'll miss your foin dinner,
But Patsy McGee has a bite and a sup
    For the 'Lily,' or Oi am a sinner."

If she had, for Thanksgiving, the bite, who can
      tell?
  You were sure of the sup, as you saw
Thro' the slush and the snow of the street, and
      the gusts
  Of the loud winds, frost-laden and raw,

The poor, draggled, smudgy Lily O'Brian,
  With the tipsiest criss-cross and reels,
Flap up the long street with her rags in the
    wind,
  And a crowd of rough boys at her heels.

"How's the 'Lily' to-day? Good luck to her
    now;
  What an illegant body she is!
I'd give just the finest jack-knife if she would
  But print on me chakes a swate kiss."

Not cruel, but thoughtless, they plucked at her
    shawl,
  And hindered her staggering way,
And caught at the tags that streamed jauntily
    out
  And her long streaming elf-locks of gray.

"Now byes, joost be lettin' the 'Lily' alone
  If ye plase, with yer blatherin' talk;
It's a moighty foin day, and Oi'd have ye's to
    know,
  The 'Lily' is out for a walk.

"I'll be crossin' the strate, and joost kape to
    yoursels,
  I'm not troublin' a soul, do ye's moind;
And plase, now, me darlints, joost let me alone,
  And don't ye's be taggin' behoind."

" There! let her alone. If you can't make her
      mad,
  It's no fun," and the hoodlums turned back;
But one, little idle, mischievous Pat,
  Still teasing, kept close in her track.

A runaway! Over the din of the winds,
  Broke the crash of the thundering feet!
Like fiends swept the horses, where Lily and
      Pat
  Halted frightened, midway of the street!

The jest turned to screams on the lips of the
      lad,
  As close to the " Lily " he clung;
" My God! They'll be killed!" but no brave
      one to help
  In all those on-lookers among!

One moment the " Lily " gazed dully around
  On the boy clinging tight to her arm;
Then she straightened, as if her brain quick-
      ened and cleared
  To the clash of the on-coming harm.

And all of the mother within her alert
  At the boy's helpless terror and cry,
She flung him to safety from under the hoofs,
  As the foam-covered steeds thundered by.

But the " Lily " crushed down in the snow and
    the mire,—
  Not an awe-stricken soul of them smiled,
As Pat kissed the blood-stained and bloated old
    face,
  But a moment before he reviled.

For the martyr's red chrism its unction had
    laid
  On the deep stains with sinfulness rife;
And angels, I know, must have gathered in
    love,
  The life yielded up for a life.

And Lily's Thanksgiving that opened at morn
  In a way that made heaven to grieve,
By the Christ-kin of pity, was crowned and
    transformed
  To a beautiful, wonderful eve.

I

THE THANKSGIVING SERMON

FROM CHANTICLEER

C. MATHEWS

The morning of the day of Thanksgiving came calm, clear and beautiful. A stillness, as of heaven and not of earth, ruled the wide landscape. The Indian Summer, which had been as a gentle mist or veil upon the beauty of the time, had gone away a little — retired, as it were, into the hills and back country, to allow the undimmed heaven to shine down upon the happy festival of families and nations. The cattle stood still in the fields without a low; the trees were quiet as in friendly recognition of the spirit of the hour; no reaper's hook or mower's scythe glanced in the meadow, no rumbling wain was on the road. The birds alone, as being more nearly akin to the feeling of the scene, warbled in the boughs.

But out of the silent gloom of the mist there sprang as by magic, a lovely illumination which lit the country far and wide, as with a thousand vari-colored lamps. As a maiden who has tarried in her chamber, some hour the least expected appears before us, apparelled in all the

pomp and hue of brilliant beauty, the fair country, flushed with innumerable tints of the
changed autumn-trees, glided forth upon the
Indian summer scene, and taught that when
kindly nature seems all foregone and spent, she
can rise from her couch fresher and more radiant than in her very prime.

What wonder if with the peep of dawn the
children leaped from bed, eager to have on their
new clothes reserved for the day, and betimes
appeared before old Sylvester in proud array
of little hats, new brightened shoes and shining
locks, span new as though they had just come
from the mint; anxious to have his grand-
fatherly approval of their comeliness? Shortly
after, the horses caught in the distant pastures,
the Captain and Farmer Oliver having charge
of them, were brought in and tied under the
trees in the door-yard.

Then, breakfast being early dispatched, there
was a mighty running to and fro of the grown
people through the house, dresses hurried from
old clothes-presses and closets, a loud demand
on every hand for pins, of which there seemed
to be (as there always is on such occasions) a
great lack. The horses were put to Mrs. Carrack's coach, the Captain's gig, the old house-
wagon, with breathless expectation on the part
of the children; and in brief, after bustling
preparation and incessant summoning of one
member of the family and another from the dif-

ferent parts of the house, all being at last ready
and in their seats, the Peabodys set forth for
the Thanksgiving Sermon at the country Meeting-house, a couple of miles away.

The Captain took the lead with his wife and
Peabody Junior somewhere and somehow between them, followed by the wagon with old
Sylvester, still proud of his dexterity as a
driver, Oliver, much pleased with the popular
character of the conveyance and wife, with
young Robert; William Peabody and wife; little Sam riding between his grandfather's legs
in front, and allowed to hold the end of the
reins. Slowly and in great state, after all
rolled Mrs. Carrack's coach with herself and
son within, and footman and coachman without.

Chanticleer, too, clear eyed and bright of
wing, walked the garden wall, carried his head
up, and acted as if he had also put on his
thanksgiving suit and expected to take the road
presently, accompany the family, and join his
voice with theirs at the little meeting-house.

Although the Captain, with his high-actioned
white horse kept out of eye-shot ahead, it was
Mrs. Carrack's fine carriage that had the triumph of the road to itself, for as it rolled glit-
tering on, the simple country people, belated
in their own preparations, or tarrying at home
to provide the dinner, ran to the windows in
wonder and admiration. The plain wagons,

bent in the same direction, turned out of the
path and gave the great coach the better half of
the way, staring a broadside as it passed.

And when the party reached the little meeting-house, what a peace hung about it! The
air seemed softer, the sunshine brighter, there,
as it stood in humble silence among the tall
trees which waved with a gentle murmur before its windows. The people, as they arrived,
glided noiselessly in, in their neat dresses and
looks of decent devotion; others as they came
made fast their horses under the sheds and
trees about — most of them in wagons and
plain chaises, brightened into all of beauty they
were capable of, by a severe attention to the
harness and mountings; others — these were a
few bachelors and striplings — trotted in
quietly on horseback. Before service a few of
the old farmers lingered outside discussing the
late crops or inquiring after each other's families, who presently went within, summoning
from the grassy churchyard — which lay next
to the meeting-house — the children who were
loitering there reading the grave-stones.

When the Captain arrived with his gig, under such extraordinary headway that he was
near driving across the grave-yard into the next
county — the country people scampered aside,
like scared fowl; Mrs. Carrack's great coach,
with its liveried outriders, set them staring as
if they did not or could not believe their own

eyes. With the arrival of old Sylvester they
re-gathered, and almost in a body, proffered
their aid to hold the horses — to help the old
Patriarch to the ground — in a word, to show
their regard and affection in every way in their
power. He tarried but a moment at the door,
to speak a word with one or two of the oldest
of his neighbors, and passed in, followed by all
of his family save Mrs. Carrack and her son,
who under color of hunting up the grave of
some old relation, delay in order to make their
appearance in the meeting-house by themselves,
and independently of the Peabody connection.

Will you pardon me, reader, if I fail to tell
you whether this house of worship was of the
Methodist, Episcopal, or Baptist creed, whether
it had a chancel or altar, or painted windows.
Whether the pews had doors to them and were
cushioned or not? Whether the minister wore
a gown and bands, or plain suit of black, or
was undistinguished in his dress? Will it not
suffice if I tell you, as the very belief of my
soul, that it was a Christian house, that there
were seats for all, that things were well intended and decently ordered, and that with a
hymn sung with such purity of heart that its
praises naturally joined in with the chiming of
the trees and the carols of the birds without
and floated on without a stop to Heaven, when
a meek man rose up:

Some two hundred years ago, our ancestors

(he said), finding themselves more comfortable in the wilderness of the new world, than they could have reasonably looked for, set apart a day of Thanksgiving to Almighty God for his manifold mercies. That day, God be praised, has been steadily observed throughout this happy land, by cheerful gatherings of families, and other festive and devotional observances, down to the present time. Our fathers covenanted, in the love of Christ, to cleave together, as brethren, however hard the brunt of fortune might be. That bond still continues. We may not live (he went on, in the very spirit and letter of the first Thanksgiving discourse ever delivered amongst us) as retired hermits, each in our cell apart, nor inquire, like David, how liveth such a man? How is he clad? How is he fed? He is my brother, we are in league together, we must stand and fall by one another. Is his labor harder than mine? Surely I will ease him. Hath he no bed to lie on? I have two — I will lend him one. Hath he no apparel? I have two suits — I will give him one of them. Eats he coarse food, bread and water, and have I better? Surely we will part stakes. He is as good a man as I, and we are bound each to other; so that his wants must be my wants; his sorrows, my sorrows; his sickness my sickness; and his welfare my welfare; for I am as he is; such a sweet sympathy were excellent, comfortable nay, heavenly, and is the only maker and conserver of churches and commonwealths."

To such as looked upon old Sylvester there seemed a glow and halo about his aged brow and whitened locks, for this was the very spirit of his life.

As though he knew the very secrets of their souls, and touched their very heart-strings with a gentle hand, the preacher glanced from one member of the Peabody household to another, as he proceeded, something in this manner. (For William Peabody:) Do I find on this holy day that I love God in all his glorious universe, more than the image even of liberty, which hath ensnared and enslaved the soul of many a man on the coin of this world? (For buxom Mrs. Jane, in her vandyke:) Do I stifle the vanity of good looks and comfortable circumstances under a plain garb? (For the jovial Captain:) Am I not over hasty in pursuit of carnal enjoyment? (For Mrs. Oliver: who was wiping her brow with the Declaration of Independence,) and eager over much for the good opinion of men, when I should be quietly serving them without report? (For Mrs. Carrack and her son:) And what are pomp and fashion, but the painted signs of good living where there is no life? These (he continued,) are all outward, mere pretences to put off our duty, and the care of our souls. Yes, we may have churches, schools, hospitals abounding —

but these are mere lath and mortar, if we have not also within our own hearts, a church where the pure worship ever goeth on, a school where the true knowledge is taught, a hospital, the door whereof standeth constantly open, into which our fellow-creatures are welcomed and where their infirmities are first cared for with all kindness and tenderness. If these be our inclinings this day, let us be reasonably thankful on this Thanksgiving morning. Let such as are in health be thankful for their good case; and such as are out of health be thankful that they are no worse. Let such as are rich be thankful for their wealth, (if it hath been honestly come by:) and let such as are poor be thankful that they have no such charge upon their souls. Let old folks be thankful for their wisdom in knowing that young folks are fools; and let young ones be thankful that they may live to see the time when they may use the same privilege. Let lean folks be thankful for their spare ribs, which are not a burthen in the harvest-field; fat folks may laugh at lean ones, and grow fatter every day. Let married folks be thankful for blessings both little and great; let bachelors and old maids be thankful for the privilege of kissing other folks' babies, and great good may it do them.

With what a glow of mutual friendship the quaint preacher was warming the plain old meeting-house on that thanksgiving day!

Finally, and to conclude, (he went on in the language of a chronicle of the time :) — Let no man look upon a turkey to-day, and say, ' This also is vanity.' What is the life of man without creature-comforts, and the stomach of the son of man with no aid from the kitchen? Despise not the day of small things, while there are pullets on the spit, and let every fowl have fair play, between the jaws of thy philosophy. Are not puddings made to be sliced, and pie-crust to be broken? Go thy ways, then, according to good sense, good cheer, good appetite, the Governor's proclamation, and every other good thing under the sun ;— render thanks for all the good things of this life, and good cookery among the rest; eat, drink, and be merry; make not a lean laudation of the bounties of Providence, but let a lively gusto follow a long grace. Feast thankfully, and feast hopingly; feast in good will to all mankind, Grahamites included; feast in the full and joyous persuasion, that while the earth remaineth, seed-time and harvest, dinner-time, pudding-time, and supper-time, are not likely to go out of fashion ;— feast with exulting confidence in the continuance of cooks, kitchens, and orthodox expounders of Scripture and the constitution in our ancient, blessed, and fat-sided commonwealth — feast, in short, like a good Christian, proving all things; relishing all things, hoping all things, expecting all

things, and enjoying all things. Let a good
stomach for dinner go hand in hand with a
good mind for sound doctrine. Let us all be
thankful that a gracious Providence hath
furnished each and all with a wholesome and
bountiful dinner this day; and, if there be none
so furnished, let him now make it known, and
we will instantly contribute thereto of our
separate abundance. There are none who
murmur — we all, therefore, have a thanksgiving dinner waiting for us; let us hie home
cheerily, and in a becoming spirit of mirth and
devotion partake thereof.

The windows of the little meeting-house
were up to let in the pleasant sunshine; and
the very horses who were within hearing of
his voice, seemed by the pricking up of their
brown ears to relish and approve of his discourse. The Captain's city nag, as wide awake
as any, seemed to address himself to an ac-
quaintance of a heavy bay plougher, who stood
at the same post, and laying their heads together for the better part of the sermon, they
appeared to regard it, as far as they caught
its meaning, as sound doctrine, particularly
acknowledging that this was as fine a thanksgiving morning as they (who had been old
friends and had spent their youth together,
being in some way related, in a farm-house in
that neighborhood) had ever known; and when
they had said as much as this, they laughed

out in very merriness of spirit, with a great whinny, as the happy audience came streaming forth at the meeting-house door. There were no cold, haughty, or distrustful faces now, as when they had entered in an hour ago; the genial air of the little meeting-house had melted away all frost of that kind; and as they mingled under the sober autumn-trees, loitering for conversation, inquiring after neighbors, old folks whose infirmities kept them at home, the young children; they seemed indeed, much more a company of brethren, embarked (as sailors say) on a common bottom for happiness and enjoyment. The children were the first to set out for home through the fields on foot; Peabody the younger, little Sam and Robert being attended by the footman in livery, whom Mrs. Carrack relieved from attendance at the rear of the coach.

If the quaint preacher had urged the rational enjoyment of the Thanksgiving cheer from the pulpit, Mopsey labored with equal zeal at home to have it worthy of enjoyment. At an early hour she had cleared decks, and taken possession of the kitchen: kindling, with dawn, a great fire in the oven for the pies, and another on the hearth for the turkey. But it was from the oven, heaping it on to the top with fresh relays of dry wood, that she expected the Thanksgiving angel to walk in all his beauty and majesty. In performance of

her duty, and from a sense only that there could
be no thanksgiving without a turkey, she
planted the tin oven on the hearth, spitted the
gobbler, and from time to time, merely as a
matter of absolute necessity, gave it a turn;
but about the mouth of the great oven she hov-
ered constantly, like a spirit — had her head in
and out at the opening every other minute;
and, when at last the pies were slided in upon
the warm bottom, she lingered there regarding
the change they were undergoing with the fond
admiration with which a connoisseur in sun-
sets hangs upon the changing colors of the
evening sky. The leisure this double duty allowed her was employed by Mopsey in scaring
away the poultry and idle young chickens
which rushed in at the back entrance of the
kitchen in swarms, and hopped with yellow
legs about the floor with the racket of constant falling showers of corn. Upon the half
door opening on the front the red rooster had
mounted, and with his head on one side observed with a knowing eye all that went forward; showing perhaps most interest in the
turning of the spit, the impalement of the
turkey thereon having been with him an object
of special consideration.

The highly colored picture of Warren at
Bunker-Hill, writhing in his death-agony on
one wall of the kitchen, and General Marion
feasting from a potato, in his tent, on the

other, did not in the least attract the attention of Mopsey. She saw nothing on the whole horizon of the glowing apartment but the pies and the turkey, and even for the moment neglected to puzzle herself, as she was accustomed to in the pauses of her daily labors, with the wonders and mysteries of an ancient dog-eared spelling-book which lay upon the smoky mantel.

Meanwhile, in obedience to the spirit of the day, the widow Margaret and Miriam, having each diligently disposed of their separate charge in the preparations, making a church of the homestead, conducted a worship in their own simple way. Opposite to each other in the little sitting-room, Miriam opened the old Family Bible, and at the widow Margaret's request read from that chapter which gives the story of the prodigal son. It was with a clear and pensive voice that she read, but not without a struggle with herself. Where the story told that the young man had gone into a far country; that he had wasted his substance in riotous living; that he was abased to the feeding of swine; that he craved in his hunger the very husks; that he lamented the plenty of his father's house — a cloud came upon her countenance, and the simplest eye could have interpreted the thoughts that troubled her. And how the fair young face brightened, when she read that the young man resolved to arise and return to the house of his father; the dear encounter; the rejoicing over his return, and the glad proclamation, "This, my son, was dead and is alive again; he was lost and is found."

"If he would come back even so," said the widow when the book was closed, "in sorrow, in poverty, in crime even, I would thank God and be grateful."

"He is not guilty, mother," Miriam pleaded, casting her head upon the widow's bosom and clinging close about her neck.

"I will not think that he is." Margaret answered, lifting up her head. "Guilty or innocent, he is my son — my son." Clasping the young orphan's hand, after a pause of tender silence, she gave utterance to her feelings in a Thanksgiving hymn. These were the words:

"Father! protect the wanderer on his way;
  Bright be for him thy stars and calm thy
    seas —
Thanksgiving live upon his lips to-day,
  And in his heart the good man's summer
    ease.

Almighty! Thou canst bring the pilgrim back,
  With a clear brow to this his childish home;
Guide him, dear Father, o'er a blameless track,
  No more to stray from us, no more to roam.

II
THE DINNER

C. MATHEWS

As the Peabody's approached the homestead,
the smoke of the kitchen chimney was visible,
circling upward and winding about in the sunshine as though it had been a delicate cork-
screw uncorking a great bottle or square old
flask of a delicious vintage. The Captain
averred a quarter of a mile away, the moment
they had come upon the brow of the hill, that
he had a distinct savor of the fragrance of the
turkey, and that it was quite as refreshing as
the first odor of the land breeze coming in from
sea, and he snuffed it up with a zeal and relish
which gave the gig an eager appetite for dinner. The Captain's conjecture was strongly
confirmed in the appearance of Mopsey, dart-
ing, with a dark face of dewy radiance at the
wood-pile and shuffling back with bustling
speed to the kitchen with a handful of delicate
splinters. "She's giving him the last turn,"
said the Captain.

The shadow of the little meeting-house was
still over the Captain, even so far away, for he
conducted the procession homeward at a pace
much less furious than that with which he had
advanced in the morning; and Mrs. Carrack
too, observed now, with a strange pleasure,

what she had given no heed to before when the fine coach was rolling in triumph along the road,— birds twittering in the sunny air by the wayside, and cattle roving like figures in a beautiful picture, upon the slopes of the distant hills.

A change, in fine, of some sort or other, had passed over every member of the Peabody family save old Sylvester, returning as going, calm, plain-spoken, straightforward and patriarchal. When they reached the gate of the homestead, William Peabody gave his hand to his wife and helped her, with some show of attention, to alight; and then there could be no doubt that it was in very truth Thanksgiving day, for the glory of the door-yard itself had paled and disappeared in the gorgeous festal light. There was no majestic gobbler in the door-yard now, with his great outspread tail, which in the proud moments of his life he would have expanded as if to shut the very light of the sun from all meaner creatures of the mansion.

Within doors there was that bustling preparation, with brief lulls of ominous silence which precede and usher in a great event. The widow Margaret, with noiseless step, glided to and fro, Miriam daintily hovering in the suburbs of the sitting-room, which is evidently the grand centre of interest, and Mopsey toils like a swart goblin in her laboratory of the kitchen in a high glow, scowling fearfully if addressed with a word which calls her attention for a moment away from her critical labors.

As the family entered the homestead on their return, the combined forces were just at the point of pitching their tent on the ground of the forthcoming engagement, in the shape of the ancient four-legged and wide leaved table, with a cover of snowy whiteness, ornamented as with shields and weapons of quaint device, in the old plates of pewter and the horn-handled knives and forks burnished to such a polish as to make the little room fairly glitter. Dishes streamed in one after the other in a long and rapid procession, piles of home-made bread, basins of apple-sauce, pickles, potatoes of vast proportion and mealy beauty. When the ancient and lordly pitcher of blue and white (whether freighted with new cider or old cold water need not be told) crowned the board, the first stage of preparation was complete, and another portentous pause ensued. The whole Peabody connection arranged in stately silence in the front parlor, looked on through the open door in wonder and expectation of what was to follow. The children loitered about the door-ways with watering eyes and open mouths, like so many innocent little dragons lying in wait to rush in at an opportune moment and bear off their prey.

And now, all at once there comes a deeper hush — a still more portentous pause — all eyes are in the direction of the kitchen; the children are hanging forward with their bodies and outstretched necks half way in at the door; Miriam and the widow stand breathless and statue-like at either side of the room; when, as if rising out of some mysterious cave in the very ground, a dark figure is discerned in the distance, about the centre of the kitchen, (into which Mopsey has made, to secure an impressive effect, a grand circuit,) head erect, and bearing before it a huge platter; all their eyes tell them, every sense vividly reports what it is the platter supports; she advances with slow and solemn step; she has crossed the sill; she has entered the sitting-room; and, with a full sense of her awful responsibility, Mopsey delivers on the table, in a cleared place left for its careful deposit, The Thanksgiving turkey.

There is no need now to sound a gong, or to ring an alarm-bell to make known to that household that dinner is ready; the brown turkey speaks a summons as with the voice of a thousand living gobblers, and Sylvester rising, the whole Peabody family flock in. To every one his place is considerately assigned, the Captain in the centre directly opposite the turkey, Mrs. Carrack on the other side, the widow at one end, old Sylvester at the head. The children too, a special exception being made in their favor to-day, are allowed seats with the grown folks, little Sam disposing himself in great comfort in his old grandsire's arms.

Another hush — for everything to-day moves on through these constantly shut and opened gates of silence, in which they all sit tranquil and speechless, when the old patriarch lifts up his aged hands over the board and repeats his customary grace:

" May we all be Christian people the day we die — God bless us."

The Captain, the great knife and fork in hand, was ready to advance.

" Stop a moment, Charley," old Sylvester spoke up. " Give us a moment to contemplate the turkey."

" I would there were just such a dish, grandfather," the Captain rejoined, " on every table in the land this day, and if I had my way there would be."

" No, no, Charley," the grandfather answered, " if there should be, there would be. There is One who is wiser than you or I."

" It would make the man who would do it," Oliver suggested, " immensely popular; he might get to be elected President of the United States."

" It would cost a large sum," remarked William Peabody, the merchant.

" Let us leave off considering imaginery turkeys, and discuss the one before us," said old

Sylvester, " but I must put a question, and if
it's answered with satisfaction, we'll proceed.
Now tell me," he said, addressing himself to
Mr. Carrack, who sat in a sort of dream, as if
he had lost his identity, as he had ever since the
night-adventure in the fez-cap and red silk
cloak: " Now tell me, Tiffany, although you
have doubtless seen a great many grand things,
has your eye fallen in with anything wherever
you traveled over the world, grander than that
Thanksgiving turkey?"

Mr. Carrack, either from excessive modesty
or total abstraction, hesitated, looked about him
hastily, and not till the Captain called across
the table, " Why don't you speak, my boy?"
and then, as if suddenly coming to, and realiz-
ing where he was, answered at last, with great
deliberation, " It *is* a fine bird."

" Enough said," spoke up old Sylvester
cheerfully; " you were the last Peabody I expected to acknowledge the merits of the
turkey:" and, looking towards the Captain
with encouragement, added, " now, knife and
fork, do your duty."

It was short work the jovial Captain made
with the prize turkey; in rapid succession plates
were forwarded, heaped, sent around; and with
a keen relish of the Thanksgiving dinner, every
head was busy. Straight on, as people who
have an allotted task before them, the Peabodys
moved through the dinner,— a powerful,

steady-going caravan of cheerful travelers, over hill, over dale, up the vallays, along the stream-side, cropping their way like a nimble-toothed flock of grazing sheep, keenly enjoying herbage and beverage by the way.

What though, while they were at the height of its enjoyment a sudden storm, at that changeful season, arose without, and dashed its heavy drops against the doors and window-panes; that only, by the contrast of security and fire-side comfort, heightened the zest within, while they were engaged with the many good dishes at least, but when another pause came, did not the pelting shower and the chiding wind talk with them, each one in turn, of the absent, and oh! some there will not believe it — the lost? It was no doubt some thought of this kind that prompted old Sylvester to speak:

"My children," said the patriarch, glancing with a calm eye around the circle of glowing faces at the table, "you are bound together with good cheer and in comfortable circumstances; and even as you, who are here from east and west, from the north and the south, by each one yielding a little of his individual whim or inclination, can thus sit together prosperously and in peace at one board, so can our glorious family of friendly States, on this and every other day, join hands, and like happy children in the fields, lead a far-lengthening

dance of festive peace among the mountains
and among the vales, from the soft-glimmering
east far on to the bright and ruddy west.

THANKSGIVING

JEANIE ROGERS SHERMAN

Dear Lord, on this way thy day of days
  Forgive me, if to thee,
In place of songs replete with praise,
This prayer alone my heart essays,
      " Work thou thy will in me."

I cannot thank thee for the pain
  With which I wait to hear
Familiar footsteps, or again
Listen for songs whose blithe refrain
      Made glad our hearts last year.

I cannot praise. Beneath thy cross
  I bow, and silently,
With eyes washed clear of much of dross,
I strive to see, above my loss,
      The joy of those with thee.

THANKSGIVING HYMN

(AIR —" AMERICA.")

O thou, whose eye of love
Looks on us from above
   Low at thy throne
We come to thee and pray
That, gleaning day by day,
Our grateful hearts alway
   Thy hand may own.

Thine are the waving fields,
Thy hand the harvest yields;
   And unto thee
To whom for rain and dew,
And skies of sunny blue,
Our love and praise are due,
   We bend the knee.

And when beneath the trees
In fairer fields than these
   Our glad feet roam,
There where the bright harps ring,
May we our gleanings bring,
And in thy presence sing
   Our harvest home.

Anon.

THANKSGIVING

EMILY READ JONES

I thank Thee that I learn
Not toil to spurn;
With all beneath the sun
It makes me one;—
For tears, whereby I gain
Kinship with human pain;
For Love, my comrade by the dusty ways,
I give Thee Praise.

FARMER JOHN'S THANKSGIVING

ISAAC F. EATON

Thanksgiving Day came chill and bare,
    The fields were brown, the trees were sere,
And snowflakes gathering in the air
    Foretold the winter of the year.
But bright the fire, and full the bin,
Each thankful heart kept glad within.

But Farmer John, with darkened brow,
    Felt not the gladness of the day;
Not to his hopes had sped the plow,
    And cherished plans had gone astray:
The wished-for gain in crop and herd,
The blight and murrain had deferred.

And to his wife he murmuring said:
  "You need not spread the feast for me;
Let others lift the thankful head
  Who for their gifts can thankful be.
My neighbors can enjoy their feast,
With herds and flocks and stores increased.

"Their every crop was full in ear,
  Their herds have gained in foal and fleece,
They weigh the balance of the year
  And laugh to count a rich increase.
For me, the months they come and go,
They find me poor, they leave me so."

And forth into the fields he went,
  Caring not where his steps might stray;
His very thought was discontent,
  His every thought reproached the day.

He passed his neighbor's garnered store,
  With envy marked his thronging herds:
His neighbor met him at the door
  With bursting heart and sobbing words.
His darling boy, his pride, his all,
Lay white beneath the funeral-pall.

     *   *   *   *

A marble mansion rose in state,
  White-walled, amid its clustering trees;
A carriage stood before the gate,
  With shining steeds and cushioned ease.

" He sure is blest," said Farmer John,
" For whom this luxury waits upon."

Within he saw the banquet spread:
   The board was set with rarest cheer;
The waiters stood at foot and head.
   He saw the owner then appear
Weak and in pain; his servants bore
Their master from his carriage door.

Smote with his sin, he blushed in shame,
   All base repinings now were still.
Content he turned the way he came,
   Back toward his own cottage sill.
With joy beneath its porch he sees
His wife, and babes about her knees.

He kissed his wife, while tears he shed;
   He clasped his babies to his breast.
" While I have strength and these," he said,
   " More than my neighbors am I blessed.
Set forth the feast! God's gifts shall raise
My heart to Him in thankful praise."

TO NOVEMBER

G. W. ADAMS

Hence, stern, grim, puritanic days,
    With nonconformist spirit rife!
I like not your forbidding ways,
    Still less your austere mode of life.

Why will you no concessions make
    To bluff old Winter's hearty cheer?
If only for old age's sake,
    He ought to be most welcome here.

Fair Summer's longing to display
    Her latest finery you kill
By cloaking her in sombre gray;—
    And spontaneity is still.

The sun makes evening sacrifice
    Of all his former trappings proud.
See how he charges in a trice
    Through straight and narrow gates of cloud!

Dissenting month of all the year!
    When you have fairly taken wing,
To skies less uniformly drear
    My true Thanksgiving song I'll sing.

MARGIE'S THANKSGIVING

E. S. BUMSTEAD

With salt and potatoes and meal for bread,
We needn't be hungry to-day," she said.
" Though I cannot stir from this queer old
    chair,
I look at the cupboard and know they're there;
And mother has left this lunch by me;
How thankful I am for it all," said she.

" With coal for the stove, and a quilt for the
    bed,
We needn't be chilly to-day," she said;
" For as long as my arms and back don't tire,
I can reach very well to feed the fire;
And mother'll be home to an early tea;
How thankful I am for it all," said she.

" There's only one thing that I really dread,
And that is the pain in my back," she said;
" But it's better, a great deal better, I know,
Than it was at the first, three months ago;
And the doctor is ever so kind to me;
How thankful I am for it all," said she.

" And by and by, when the winter is dead,
He thinks I'll be almost well," she said;
" And I'll have some crutches and walk, and
    then

I can get the dinners for mother again;
And, oh! how glad and happy we'll be!
How thankful I am for it all," said she.

———

THE OLD NEW ENGLAND THANKS-GIVING

HARRIET BEECHER STOWE

* * * * * *

The king and high priest of all festivals was the autumn Thanksgiving. When the apples were all gathered and the cider was all made, and the yellow pumpkins were rolled in from many a hill in billows of gold, and the corn was husked, and the labors of the season were done, and the warm, late days of Indian Summer came in, dreamy, and calm, and still, with just enough frost to crisp the ground of a morning, but with warm traces of benignant, sunny hours at noon, there came over the community a sort of genial repose of spirit,— a sense of something accomplished, and of a new golden mark made in advance,— and the deacon began to say to the minister, of a Sunday, " I suppose it's about time for the Thanksgiving proclamation."

WE THANK THEE

RALPH WALDO EMERSON

For flowers that bloom about our feet;
For tender grass, so fresh, so sweet;

For song of bird, and hum of bee;
For all things fair we hear or see,
    Father in heaven, we thank Thee!

For blue of stream and blue of sky;
For pleasant shade of branches high;
For fragrant air and cooling breeze;
For beauty of the blooming trees,
    Father in heaven, we thank Thee!

GIVE THANKS FOR WHAT?

W. F. CROFFUT

"Let Earth give thanks," the deacon said,
And then the proclamation read.

"Give thanks fer what, an' what about?"
Asked Simon Soggs when church was out.
"Give thanks fer what? I don't see why;
The rust got in an' spiled my rye,
And hay wan't half a crop, and corn
All wilted down and looked forlorn;
The bugs jest gobbled my pertaters,
The what-you-call-em *lineaters,*
And gracious! when you come to wheat,
There's more than all the world can eat;
Onless a war should interfere,
Crops won't bring half a price this year;
I'll hev to give 'em away, I reckon!"

" Good for the poor!" exclaimed the deacon.

" Give thanks fer what?" asked Simon Soggs,
" Fer th' freshet carryin' off my logs?
Fer Dobbin goin' blind? Fer five
Uv my best cows, that was alive
Afore the smashin' railroad come
And made it awful troublesome?
Fer that hay-stack the lightnin' struck
And burnt to ashes? — thund'rin luck!
Fer ten dead sheep?" sighed Simon Soggs.

The deacon said, " You've got yer hogs!"

" Give thanks? And Jane and baby sick?
I e'enmost wonder if ole Nick
Ain't runnin' things!"

              The deacon said,
" Simon! yer people *might be dead!*"

" Give thanks?" said Simon Soggs again,
" Jest look at what a fix we're in!
The country's rushin' to the dogs
At race-horse speed!" said Simon Soggs,
" Rotten all through — in every State,—
Why, ef we don't repudiate,
We'll hev to build, fer big and small,
A poor-house that'll hold us all.
All round the crooked whiskey still
Is runnin' like the devil's mill;

Give thanks? How mad it makes me feel,
To think how office-holders steal!
The taxes paid by you and me
Is four times bigger'n they should be;
The Fed'ral Gov'ment's all askew,
The ballot's sech a mockery, too!
Some votes too little, some too much,
Some not at all — it beats the Dutch!
And now no man knows what to do,
Or how is how, or who is who.
Deacon! corruption's sure to kill!
This ' glorious Union ' never will,
I'll bet a continental cent,
Elect another President!
Give thanks fer *what*, I'd like to know? "

The deacon answered, sad and low,
" Simon! it fills me with surprise,
Ye don't see whar yer duty lies;
Kneel right straight down, in all the muss,
And thank God that it ain't no wuss! "

SOMETHING TO BE THANKFUL FOR

CLARA J. DENTON

I'm glad that I am not to-day
    A chicken or a goose,
Or any other sort of bird
    That is of any use.

I rather be a little girl,
　　Although 'tis very true,
The things I do not like at all,
　　I'm often made to do.

I rather eat some turkey than
　　To be one, thick and fat,
And so, with all my heart, to-day,
　　I'll thankful be for that.

GIVING THANKS

For the hay and the corn and wheat that is
　　reaped,
For the labor well done, and the barns that are
　　heaped,
For the sun and the dew and the sweet honey-
　　comb,
For the rose and the song, and the harvest
　　brought home —
　　　　Thanksgiving! Thanksgiving!
For the trade and the skill and the wealth in
　　our land,
For the cunning and strength of the working-
　　man's hand,
For the good that our artists and poets have
　　taught,
For the friendship that hope and affection have
　　brought —
　　　　Thanksgiving! Thanksgiving!

For the homes that with purest affection **are**
    blest,
For the season of plenty and well deserved rest,
For our country extending from sea to sea,
The land that is known as the "Land of the
    Free"—
        Thanksgiving! Thanksgiving!
                                        Anon.

———

THANKSGIVING DAY

The year decays, November's blast
    Through leafless boughs pipes shrill **and**
        drear;
With warmer love the home clasps fast
    The hands, the hearts, the friends most dear.
On many seas men sail the fleet
    Of hopes as fruitless as the foam;
They roam the world with restless feet,
    But find no sweeter spot than home.

To-day with quickened hearts they hear
    Old times, old voices chime and call;
The dreams of many a vanished year
    Sit by them at this festival.
Though hearts that warmed them once are cold,
    Though heads are hoar with winter frost
That once were bright with tangled gold —
    Thanks for the blessings kept or lost.

Thanks for the strong, free wind of life,
  However it change or veer;
For the love of mother and sister and wife;
  Clear stars that to haven steer;
For the quenchless lamps of changeless love
  That burn in the night of the dead;
For the life that is, for the hope above,
  Be thanksgiving by all hearts said.

Anon.

IV

THE THANKSGIVING SEASON

ODE TO AUTUMN

JOHN KEATS

Season of mists and mellow fruitfulness!
Close bosom-friend of the maturing sun;
Conspiring with him how to load and bless
With fruit the vines that round the thatch-eaves
    run;
To bend with apples the moss'd cottage trees,
And fill all fruit with ripeness to the core;
To swell the gourd, and plump the hazel shells
With a sweet kernel; to set budding more,
And still more, later flowers for the bees,
Until they think warm days will never cease,
For Summer has o'er-brimmed their clammy
    cells.

Who hath not seen thee oft amid thy store?
Sometimes whoever seeks abroad may find
Thee sitting careless on a granary-floor,
Thy hair soft lifted by the winnowing wind;
Or, on a half-reap'd furrow sound asleep,
Drowsed with the fume of poppies, while thy
    hook
Spares the next swath and all its twinéd flow-
    ers;

And sometimes like a gleaner thou dost keep
Steady thy laden head across a brook;
Or by a cider-press, with patient look,
Thou watchest the last oozings, hours by hours.

Where are the songs of Spring? Ay, where
    are they?
Think not of them; thou hast thy music, too,
While barréd clouds bloom the soft-dying day,
And touch the stubble plains with rosy hue;
Then in a wailful choir the small gnats mourn
Among the river swallows, borne aloft
Or sinking as the light wind lives or dies;
And full-grown lambs loud bleat from hilly
    bourn;
Hedge-crickets sing; and now with treble soft
The redbreast whistles from a garden croft,
And gathering swallows twitter in the skies.

INDIAN SUMMER

EUDORA S. BUMSTEAD

The grain is gathered in;
The season's work is done;
No more the hurrying din
Of the stress of noon-time sun.
But beautiful and calm,
And full of healing balm,
The autumn rest is won.

Yea, the tired world standeth still
In a trance of peace and praise;
And the light on field and hill
Is the light of bygone days;
And long-forgotten rhymes
And songs of the dear old times
Come back in the brooding haze.

Fair is the passing day
When the sun so kindly beams:
Fair is the far-away,
And the world that only seems;
O, naught in the round, ripe year
Is so strange and sweet and dear
As this beautiful time of dreams.

IN NOVEMBER

SUSAN KELLY PHILLIPS

Soft, sweet, and sad in its pathetic glory,
The pale November sunshine floods the earth,
Like a bright ending to a mournful story,
Or, in a minor tune, a chord of mirth.

Before the wet west wind forever drifting,
The falling leaves fly o'er the garden walks;
The wet west wind the bare, gaunt branches lift-
ing,
And bowing to black mold the withered stalks.

The blackbird whistles to the lingering thrushes,
The wren chirps welcome to the hardy tit,
While the brave robin, 'neath the holly-brushes,
Sees what of berried store still gleams for it.

And the heart, sad for vanished hopes, in turning
Back to lost summers from the winter's chill,
Sees the rich promise through the weary yearn-
ing,
That heaven and spring will each our trust ful-
fill.

———

A DAY OF THE INDIAN SUMMER

SARAH HELEN WHITMAN

A day of golden beauty! Through the night
The hoar-frost gathered, o'er each leaf and
spray
Weaving its filmy network; thin and bright,
And shimmering like silver in the ray
Of the soft sunny morning; turf and tree
Pranct in its delicate embroidery,
And every withered stump and mossy stone,
With gems incrusted and with seed-pearl sown;
While in the hedge the frosted berries glow,
The scarlet holly and the purple sloe,
And all is gorgeous, fairy-like and frail
As the famed gardens of the Arabian tale.

How soft and still the autumnal landscape lies,
Calmly outspread beneath the smiling skies;
As if the earth, in prodigal array
Of gems and broidered robes kept holiday;
Her harvest yielded and her work all done,
Basking in beauty 'neath the autumn sun!

THE INDIAN SUMMER

JOHN H. BRYANT

That soft autumnal time
Is come, that sheds, upon the naked scene,
Charms only known in this our northern
    clime —
    Bright seasons, far between.

The woodland foliage now
Is gathered by the wild November blast;
E'en the thick leaves upon the poplar's bough
    Are fallen, to the last.

The mighty vines, that round
The forest trunks their slender branches bind,
Their crimson foliage shaken to the ground,
    Swing naked in the wind.

Some living green remains
By the clear brook that shines along the lawn;
But the sear grass stands white o'er all the
    plains,
    And the bright flowers are gone.

V

THANKSGIVING EXERCISES

IN HONOR OF THANKSGIVING

LIZZIE M. HADLEY

For Twelve Boys and Twenty-one Girls.

Directions: This exercise should be performed by eleven girls, twelve boys and ten little girls from the primary class. Decorate the room with flags, pine boughs, evergreens, corn, jack-o'-lanterns, etc. If given in a school-room, upon the blackboard sketch the Mayflower, Pilgrim houses, chairs, Peregrine White's cradle, kettles, lanterns, etc. Also outline a map showing Pilgrims' starting point, route and landing place. The boys and girls march around the school-room and upon the rostrum in time to lively music. On reaching the stage they arrange themselves in a semicircle and as each one recites he or she steps out of the circle to the center of the stage, returning to place at close of reciting. Costumes: The Pilgrims wear dark clothes; the girls, caps, kerchiefs and cuffs made of white paper, and the boys round collars and cuffs of the same material. The Dutch girls' costumes can be copied from pictures and may be made of tissue paper of cheap cambric. Old English costumes may be copied and made in the same way.

Recitation for All.

When November's gusty breezes
  Shake the branches bare and brown
And you hear on sunny uplands,
  Ripened nuts come dropping down,

While the loaded wains are creaking
　'Neath a weight they scarce can hold,
And you see each bin and storehouse
　Brimming o'er with Nature's gold,
Then the nation's sons and daughters,
　Where so e'er their feet may stray
Turn their eager footsteps homeward,
　There to keep Thanksgiving Day.

First English Girl. Thanksgiving Day is
one of the oldest festivals of which we have any
knowledge, and its origin is lost in the days
of myth and fable. But, we know that each
autumn the Romans held Thanksgiving feasts
in honor of the goddess Ceres, while the Greeks
at about the same time honored the god Demeter in the same fashion.

Second English Girl. The Israelites, also,
set apart days for Thanksgiving.

First English Boy. The oldest recorded one
is the Feast of Tabernacles.

Second English Boy. In later times these
days have been appointed for deliverance from
evil, famine, drouth, perhaps an enemy, or some
special blessing received.

Dutch Girl. We had a Thanksgiving Day
in Leyden Oct. 3, 1575, the first anniversary
after its siege by the Spaniards.

Third English Boy. September 3, 1588, was
a day of Thanksgiving in my country, for the
defeat of the Spanish Armada.

Third English Girl. Another English Thanksgiving Day was February 27, 1872, to give thanks for the restoration to health of the Prince of Wales.

English Boys and Girls, together. June 27, 1887, was Thanksgiving Day in England, for the Queen's Jubilee.

Pilgrim Boys and Girls together. Thanksgivings in this country date from the first settlement of the country, and, we, the Pilgrim boys and girls, have come to tell you why we kept those days, almost three hundred years ago.

Boy. I am not a Pilgrim, I belong to the Coopham colony that settled at the mouth of Kennebec river, in Maine in 1607, but I helped keep the first Thanksgiving in what is now the great United States. The winter of 1607 we nearly died of cold and hunger. When a ship appeared in the spring-time we had a day of Thanksgiving. But soon after this we became discouraged and went back to England.

First Pilgrim Girl. We, too, suffered from cold and hunger. We always spoke of that winter as the " starving time." But we did not think of going back to England even when half our number died.

First Pilgrim Boy. We were brave men and women, and the living ones, like real soldiers, closed up the ranks when their friends and neighbors fell by the way.

Second Pilgrim Girl. In the spring we worked hard, and planted corn, peas and barley.

Second Pilgrim Boy. When autumn came our crops were so fine that our good Governor Bradford appointed a day of Thanksgiving.

Third Pilgrim Girl. Perhaps you will think we hadn't much for which to give thanks. There were twenty acres of corn and six each of peas and barley. But we knew that from these there would be food enough to keep us through the long winter and that there would be no " starving time " again. Besides we had warm houses and comfortable clothes, so we " thanked God and took courage " and kept Thanksgiving Day.

Third Pilgrim Boy. Our next Thanksgiving Day was in 1623. It was so dry and hot that summer that we feared our crops would die, so we appointed a day for fasting and prayer, and for nine hours we besought God to help us.

Fourth Pilgrim Girl. At first it was bright sunshine, then came little clouds, and by and by the rain began to fall, and our crops were saved.

Fourth Pilgrim Boy. The Indians who knew what was going on, said, The God of the white man has heard their prayers.

Fifth Pilgrim Girl. In 1633 the Massachusetts Bay colony set apart a day for Thanksgiving.

First Dutch Boy. William Kieft, governor of New Netherlands, appointed a Thanksgiving Day in 1644, and again in 1645.

Second Dutch Girl. In 1655 Peter Stuyvesant appointed a Thanksgiving Day for victory obtained over the Swedes around Delaware Bay.

Second Dutch Boy. The first national Thanksgiving was for the declaration of peace in 1784.

Fifth Pilgrim Boy. Thanksgiving Day was held in 1789 to commemorate the adoption of the Constitution.

Sixth Pilgrim Girl. In 1795 Washington appointed a day of Thanksgiving for the suppression of the Whiskey Insurrection.

Sixth Pilgrim Boy. A day of Thanksgiving was appointed at the conclusion of the second war with England in 1814.

All. After 1817 Thanksgiving Days were appointed by the different governors of the states but since 1863 it has been a national holiday appointed by the president, and supplemented by the governors. Every one who really loves his country will do his best to honor and perpetuate the day.

March to seats to lively music. Ten little girls from the primary class now come to positions near the maps or black board sketches. Each one takes the pointer and indicates the proper picture as she recites her lines. At the

close she hands the pointer to the next child and
sits down near by.

First (pointing to starting point of Mayflower.)
    This is the land so far away,
    Where started the germ of Thanksgiving
       Day.

Second.
    These are the Pilgrims who sailed the sea,
    To found a nation for you and me.

Third.
    This is the Mayflower staunch and true
    In which they sailed over the ocean blue.

Fourth.
    This is the route, where, day by day,
    To an unknown country they made their way.

Fifth.
    Here is Plymouth Rock where they stood.
    And called the land they had come to
      " Good."

Sixth.
    Here is a house of logs and clay,
    The shelter from cold they built one day.

Seventh.
    Here is the captain of great renown,
    Stout Miles Standish of Plymouth town.

Eighth.
    Here is Priscilla, the saucy young elf,
    And Alden, she told to "speak for himself."

Ninth.
    Here are the chairs, still safely kept
    And the cradle where baby Peregrine slept.

Tenth.

Would you like to see more? Then come
   with me
To that old town standing beside the sea.
There you will find them, things galore
The Pilgrims bore to the new world's shore.

Song by School, Air " America."

Ruler of land and sea
Hear us we lift to Thee
   Our hearts alway
For guidance through life's maze
For health and length of days
We come with songs of praise
         Thanksgiving Day.

THANKSGIVING EXERCISE

LIZZIE M. HADLEY

GIRLS.

Oh, time keeps steadily on and on
   And the years go round and round,
But the best and brightest day of all,
   In *November's* always found.

BOYS.

The best and brightest day of all?
   Is it better than Fourth of July,
When cannons roar and crackers pop,
   And rockets blaze in the sky?

First Girl.

Oh, Fourth of July is well enough,
But it's only a day for *boys,*
When with drum and fife they march along,
All trying to make a noise.

First Boy.

Well, what is the day so bright and fair
That comes when the year is old,
When trees are bare and snowflakes fall
And the wind blows fierce and cold?

Second Girl.

" It is the Puritan's Thanksgiving Day,
And gathered home from fresher homes
around,
The old man's children keep the holiday,
In dear New England, since the fathers slept,
The sweetest holiday of all the year, Bitter
Sweet."

All the Girls.

Oh, that is the day we like the best,
A time for mirth, and for play,
When merry and glad we celebrate,
Our happy *Thanksgiving Day.*

Third Girl.

Then mother Nature's kindly hand
    Fills to the brim her plenteous horn,
And scattered o'er a smiling land
    Stand golden shocks of ripened corn.

Fourth Girl.

" And victorious Hiawatha
    Stripped the garments from Mondaime,
    And laid him in the earth, and made it
    Soft and loose, and light above him,
    And at length, a small green feather,
    From the earth shot slowly upwards,
    Then another and another
    And before the Summer ended,
    Stood the *maize* in all its beauty,
    And still later, when the Autumn
    Changed the long green leaves to yellow,
    And the soft and juicy kernals,
    Grew like wampum hard and yellow,
    Then the ripened ears he gathered,
    Stripped the withered leaves from off them
    And made known unto the people
    This new gift of the Great Spirit."

                      Longfellow.

All the Girls.

" But let the good old crop adorn
    The hills our fathers trod,

Still let us for his golden corn
  Send up our thanks to God."

                                        Whittier.

FIFTH GIRL.

Such bounteous store of garnered grain
  Our bursting barns can scarcely hold,
And gleaming now in every field
  We see the pumpkins' globes of gold.

SIXTH GIRL.

" Oh, fruit loved of childhood! the old days re-
    calling,
When wood grapes were purpling and brown
    nuts were falling,
When wild ugly faces we carved in its skin
Glared out through the dark with a candle
    within,
When we laughed round the corn-heap with
    hearts all in tune,
Our chair a broad pumpkin, our lantern the
    moon,
Telling tales of the fairy who traveled like
    steam
In a pumpkin-shell coach with two rats for her
    team."

                                        Whittier.

ALL THE GIRLS.

So gladly we welcome the happy day,
    That comes when the summer is o'er,
When the scattered friends we love so well,
    Round the home hearth meet once more.

BOYS.

And I'm sure we boys all like it well
    And are glad when the time draws near,
But can any one tell *why* we celebrate
    This one day in the year?

FIRST GIRL.

Oh, into the past the years have fled,
    Till centuries high they're piled,
Since the brave little band of Puritans
    Sailed over the ocean wild.

Over the surging, pathless sea,
    They sailed to the unknown West,
Home and kindred behind them lay
    But they loved their Lord the best.

SECOND GIRL.

Then bitter and cold from his icy home,
    Came the North wind's biting breath,
And part of that brave little Pilgrim band
    Grew silent and cold in death.

Third Girl.

But slowly and surely on and on,
　　The months crept day by day,
They mourned their dead, yet the remnant
　　　　brave
　　Kept steadily on their way.

All.

Oh, cruel time! When all the world
　　Lay white beneath the drifting snow,
When famine boldly stalked about,
　　And every tree-trunk hid a foe.

Fourth Girl.

But though stern winter's icy reign
　　Was bitter, yet at length 'twas past,
And heralded by singing birds,
　　The glorious spring-time came at last.

Fifth Girl.

Feeble and weak that little band,
　　They plowed the soil and sowed the seed,
And then with trusting hearts they prayed,
　　That God would help them in their need.

All the Girls.

The prayer of faith is always heard,
　　And summer sunshine, dew and rain,

God freely gave till all the fields
    Were white with ripened golden grain.

SIXTH GIRL.

And when once more the autumn woods,
    With purple, red, and gold grew gay,
The little band of Puritans
    Together kept Thanksgiving Day.

ALL.

" Our harvest being gotten in, our governor
sent four men on fowling, so that we might in
a special manner rejoice together, after we had
gathered the fruit of our labors."

RECITATION

" And now," said the governor, gazing abroad
    on the piled up store
Of the sheaves that dotted the clearings and
    covered the meadow's o'er,
'Tis meet that we render praises because of this
    yield of grain;
'Tis meet that the Lord of the harvest be
    thanked for His sun and rain."

" And therefore I, William Bradford (by the
    grace of God to-day,

And the franchise of this good people), Governor of Plymouth say
Thro' virtue of vested power — ye shall gather with one accord,
And hold in the month of November, thanksgiving unto the Lord.

" He hath granted us peace and plenty, and the quiet we've sought so long;
He hath thwarted the wily savage, and kept him from doing us wrong;
And unto our feast the Sachem shall be bidden, that he may know
We worship his own Great Spirit who maketh the harvest grow.

" So shoulder your matchlocks, masters; there is hunting of all degrees;
And fishermen, take your tackle, and scour for spoil the seas;
And maidens and dames of Plymouth, your delicate crafts employ
To honor our First Thanksgiving, and make it a feast of joy."

Margaret J. Preston.

ALL.

So now when Autumn doffs her robes
Of purple, and green, and gold;

When the trees stand leafless, bare, and
　　brown,
　And the nights grow bleak and cold;

Again we come together all
　To keep in the good old way,
Just as they did in days of yore,
　A glad Thanksgiving Day.

———

GRANNY'S STORY

A MONOLOGUE

EMILY HUNTINGTON MILLER

The speaker should wear black dress, white cap and
kerchief.

Yes, lads, I'm a poor old body,
　My wits are not over clear
I can't remember the day o' the week,
　And scarcely the time o' year,
But one thing is down in my mem'ry
　So deep it is sure to stay:
It was long ago but it all comes back
　As if it happened to-day.

Here, stand by the window, laddies,
　Do you see, away to the right,
A long, black line on the water,
Topped with a crest of white?

That is the reef Defiance
  Where the good ship Gasperau
Beat out her life in the breakers
  Just fifty-six years ago.

I mind 'twas a raw Thanksgiving,
  The sleet drove sharp as knives,
And most of us, here at the barbor,
Were sailors' sweethearts and wives.
But I had my goodman beside me,
  And every thing tidy and bright,
When all of a sudden a signal
  Shot up through the murky night.

And a signal gun in the darkness
  Boomed over and over again,
As if it bore, in its awful tone,
  The shrieks of women and men.
And down to the rocks we crowded
  Facing the icy rain,
Praying the Lord to be their aid,
Since human help was in vain.

Then my goodman stooped and kissed me,
  And said, " It is but to die:
Who goes with me to the rescue? "
  And six noble lads cried, " I."
And crouching there in the tempest
  Hiding our faces away
We heard them row into the blackness
  And what could we do but pray?

So long — when at last their cheering
   Came faintly above the roar
I thought I had died and in heaven
   My trouble and grief were o'er.
And the white-faced women and children,
   All seemed like ghosts in my sight,
As the boats, weighed down to the water,
   Came tossing into the light.

And little we cared that the breakers
   Were tearing the ship in their hold,
There are things, if you weigh them fairly,
   Will balance a mint of gold.
And even the bearded captain
   Said, " Now let the good ship go,
Since never a soul that sailed with me
   Goes down in the Gaspereau."

Eh! that was a heartsome Thanksgiving
   With sobbing and laughter and prayers,
Our lads with their brown, dripping faces
   And not a face missing from theirs.
For you never can know how much dearer
   The one you love dearest can be
Till you've had him come back to you
     safely,
   From out of the jaws of the sea.

Yes, stand by the windows, laddies,
   Now, look away to the right,
And learn from that reef Defiance,
   The lesson I learned that night,

To make a heartsome Thanksgiving,
    Just for the loved ones so near,
For them a gladsome Thanksgiving,
    That will last the whole long year.

WE THANK THEE

First pupil.

For gainful hours of pain and loss,
For strength that grew beneath the cross,
For gold refined and freed from dross,
    We thank thee, Lord.

Second pupil.

For cheerful ease and calm content,
For hours in gentle gladness spent,
So sweet we ask not how they went —
    We thank thee, Lord.

Third pupil.

For hours o'erlived with bated breath;
For victory in the fight with death;
For answered prayers that strengthened faith;
    We thank thee, Lord.

Fourth pupil.

For ties thou hast not torn apart;
For glimpses of thee as thou art;
For the "bright weather of our heart,"
    We thank thee, Lord.

Fifth pupil.

And, oh! for mercies numberless —
For succor in our soul's distress,
In perils we but dimly guess,
    We thank thee, Lord.

The five together.

We have no words and little wit
To frame such thanks as may befit
Thy grace, and yet — thou knowest it —
    We thank thee, Lord.

As children sometimes suddenly
Run, grateful, to a father's knee —
We dimly feel our debt to thee,
    And thank thee, Lord.

                        Anon.

POETIC RESPONSES.

(Let 12 girls representing the months ask the questions of 12 boys. The boys should be dressed as farmers, and carry rake, hoe, fork, etc.)

Girls.

Have you cut the wheat in the blowing fields,
    The barley, the oats, and the rye?
The golden corn and the pearly rice?
    For the winter days are nigh.

Boys.

We have reaped them all from shore to shore,
And the grain is safe on the threshing floor.

Girls.

Have you gathered the berries from the vines,
  And the fruit from the orchard trees?
The dew and the scent from the rose and thyme
  In the hive of the honey bees?

Boys.

The peach and the plum and the apple are
    ours,
And the honeycomb from the scented flowers.

Girls.

The wealth of the snowy cotton field
  And the gift of the sugar cane,
The savory herb and the nourishing root?
  There has been nothing given in vain.

Boys.

We have gathered the harvest from shore to
    shore
And the measure is full and running o'er.

Girls and boys.

Then lift up the head with a song!
  And lift up the head with a gift!
To the ancient giver of all
  The spirit in gratitude lift!
For the joy and the promise of spring,
  For the hay and the clover sweet,
The barley, the rye, and the oats,
  The rice and the corn and the wheat,

The cotton and sugar and fruit,
    The flowers and the fine honeycomb,
The country, so fair and so free,
    The blessing and glory of home.

    The whole school.
Thanksgiving! thanksgiving! thanksgiving!
    Joyfully, gratefully call
To God, the ' Preserver of men,'
    The bountiful father of all.

———

THANKSGIVING IN THE PAST AND PRESENT

MARION S. BLAISDELL

Characters

Ceres.	Spirits of the Past.
Demeter.	Jewess.
Harvest Home.	Indian.
Thanksgiving.	Child.

FOR TABLEAUX

Greeks, Romans, Indians, and Puritans.

SCENE

An ordinary room.   Table with books, wand, globe, and reading-glass.   History sits with one hand upon the globe.   Child on a low stool or cushion at her feet.

COSTUMES

Ceres, or Demeter, wears a white gown and a gilt girdle.   As Ceres, she wears a crown of corn and grain; as Demeter, a wreath of ivy leaves.

Harvest Home.   Short, full skirt reaching to the ankles; close-fitting tunic; hair in long plaits; a crown of fruits, grains, and leaves.

243

Jewess. A loose robe of some bright color. Costume may be copied from a biblical print.

Indian. A band of feathers on the head; a blanket around the shoulders; beaded leggings and moccasins, and a short feather-trimmed skirt. Copy Puritan costume from old prints. The wood-cuts found in most histories will answer.

Spirits. White gowns; a gilt star upon their foreheads. A wire foundation may be covered with white gauze and fastened to the shoulders for wings.

Sounds of music outside. Voices singing: Air "Ensemble" from "Pinafore."

> All hail the day we celebrate!
> The day appointed by the state,
> When friends who far away do roam,
> Now seek once more their native home;
>   We love this happy day.

> New England's feast, the first and best
> By every state 'tis now confessed
> And when $\left\{\begin{array}{l}\text{I see}\\\text{we see}\end{array}\right\}$ the day come round
>   In merry roundelay.

> $\left\{\begin{array}{l}\text{I'll}\\\text{We'll}\end{array}\right\}$ sing its praise to all around

History:

> Ah, me! how the years to the past have
> gone
> And how changed are the scenes I look
> upon.
> Since first my cradle was rocked on the
> earth
> When in beautiful Eden I had my birth!

Child: Were you in fair Eden?

History: Yes, child, I came

> To earth when sin was only a name.
> I saw the first pair that awful day
> They were driven from Eden's gates away,
> When the vials of wrath on their heads were
> poured
> And the gate was barred by a flaming sword.
> O, the years by thousands have passed since
> then,
> Yet still I dwell in the haunts of men,
> And 'tis I who have chronicled every deed
> That on history's page you now may read.

> *Child:* Since you are so wise,
> Then tell us, I pray,
> Something about
> Our Thanksgiving day.

History: (*Holds up glass and looks through it.*)

> Ah, child! I look back all the wearisome
> years,

Through my magical lens, and lo! there
 appears
Full many a scene in that day's history;
So, to tell of each one, I will summon for
 thee
The spirits, whose duties are but to por-
 tray
The legends belonging to Thanksgiving
 day.
   (*Waves her wand.*)
Come from the past,
O spirits immortal!
Leave the dead years
And come back to life's portal.
There, with your magic art,
Weave o'er and o'er
·Spells that shall bring back
The old days once more.

(*Music outside. Enter spirits, singing. Air,
Chorus from " Yeoman of the Guard.*")

Spirits: Here we come, O History!
   Sing, sing merrily!
   We'll rehearse the mystery,
   Sing, sing cheerily.

   We will waken days of old,
   Their old tales shall be retold,
   Thus to you we'll bring
   Days their songs to sing.
   (*All bow before History.*)

Spirits: We have all heard thy summons
        And all have obeyed.
        We have come at thy bidding —
        Not one has delayed,
        From Palestine's hills,
        From Greece and from Rome.
        And e'en from old England
        We bring "Harvest Home."
        And with them, in skins
        And feathers all dressed,
        A gay, painted savage
        You'll find here confessed.

Child: Is that all?

Spirits: Nay the last,
        Yet by no means the least,
        Slow marching along,
        Comes the Puritan feast,

Child: And still are there others?

Spirits: Yes, this was the way.
        They thanked God for blessings
        In that elder day.
        Thus, one after one,
        Did Thanksgivings appear,
        And now with the Autumn
        They come every year.
        Would you hear of these feasts,
        And the curious ways,
        Of the people who started
        Your Thanksgiving days?

Child: Yes, tell us some stories,
   Some legend or song,
   Or myths that back
   In that old past belong.

Spirit: Approach now, fair Ceres,
   Thou goddess of grain.
   Throw off the long years.
   And appear in our train.

Ceres: 'Tis a long and weary journey from that old time down to the present hour, but you have called me, gentle spirits, and I must obey the summons. What is your will?

Spirits: In the old heathen times,
   Thou goddess of Rome,
   Canst tell how this feast
   Was kept at thy home?

Ceres (*sadly*): Ah, those old festal days! There is naught now can compare with them. The great feast of Cerelia, so named in my honor, came in October, at the ingathering of the harvest. It was a season of relaxation, alike for rich and poor, patrician and plebeian. Then we cast our cares aside, and mirth and rejoicing prevailed.

Our young men and our maidens, crowned with poppies and corn leaves, marched in processions and engaged in rustic games and sports.

Our household gods were crowned with flowers.
Our temples were decked with garlands of
fruits, grains, and leaves; our altars smoked
with incense and the best of our fruits and
grains were offered to our gods. Alas, for
Rome! Her glory has departed. Those old
days are gone forever, and I, then so honored,
am now called a myth, and the maidens and
youths of to-day say that I only lived in the
imagination of the people.

> Thus, changing fashions on us fall
> And time, the great magician, changeth all.

History:
> Your lot is a sad one; yet, Ceres, remember
> The plant that you started blooms every
>   November.

Spirits: Demeter, come hither.

Child: Why, this is the same
> Who left us but now!
> Has she changed her name?

Spirits: Yes when from old Greece she re-
>   moved,
> With the nation,
> She changed then her name,
> But retained still the station
> The gods had assigned her,

As goddess of grain.
Yet, the name matters little.
Come hither again,
And tell us, fair goddess,
When they were at peace,
How they kept this great
Festival in old Greece.

Demeter: Lo, I am here. Ceres of Rome; Demeter, the Grecian goddess of cornfields and harvests. You seem surprised, O mortal! to behold me once more, and from another country and bearing another name. But of old my home was in Greece, where I was loved and honored by the people. It was I who taught them to plough the ground, sow the seeds and to gather for their needs the ripened harvests. For this work they chose me their patron deity, and each year, after the September harvests, in my honor, they celebrated their greatest feast.

Child: When they'd gathered their grapes,
Their corn and their oil,
How named they this feast
That lightened their toil?

Demeter: They called it the Thalysia, and all save barbarians and murderers might take part in the solemn festivities, which lasted for nine days.

Child: Now, surely, these Grecians had curious
ways!
What rites could they have to last for
nine days?

Demeter: Those who conducted the worship
in my honor were styled the mycæ, and on the
first and second of these festal days they assembled at Athens and underwent purification.
They fasted on the third day, and then broke
their fast with honey-cakes and a posset of bar-
ley-meal and mint. Then came the day of sacrifices, when they offered upon their altars their
honey-oil, milk, and the fruits of the soil.

Child: Proceed, fair Demeter, we listen to you,
What other and curious things did they
do?

Demeter: On the fifth a strange, mystic
night procession of torch-bearers marched along
the sacred way from Athens to Eleusis. Then
came the sixth day, the crown of all the others.
Then thousands of worshippers in their festal
robes decked with garlands and bearing torches
chanted my praises. The remaining days were
spent in sports, sacrifices, and in feasting. Ah,
we ne'er shall see such days again! The world
has gained wisdom, but it has lost its graceful
poesy, and cares for naught but prose. Our

mystic rites no longer charm the senses. Small
wonder that the sun of Greece has set.

History: Behold! where a shadow from out
the dead years, a scene from this festal time
now appears.

Tableau I

(Greeks and Romans with lighted torches marching around an altar, with fruits heaped around a fire
in the centre. The altar may be made of boxes piled
above one another, and a dark cloth thrown over
them. An earthen dish containing a small quantity
of alcohol, placed in the centre of the altar, may be
hidden from the audience by the fruits heaped around
it. When ready to show the tableau, set fire to the
alcohol.)

History: It is gone like a dream,
    Or the mist from the sea.
    Now, spirits, whom next
    Wilt thou call unto thee?

Spirits:
 We will call to the people, who sit now for-
   lorn
 In sackcloth and ashes, their glory all gone.
 O Jews! who by Babylon's waters oft wept,
 Tell us how in your day they festivals kept.

Jewess (steps to front of stage):
    When the God they adored,
    Who dwelleth in heaven?

To His chosen people
Of His plenty had given;
When they'd garnered the grains
Bending 'neath their ripe load,
Then, to give God their thanks
For His bounties bestowed,
From desert, from hillside,
From lone mountain crest,
All over the land,
From the east to the west,
The people came marching,
A slow pilgrim throng,
Straight on to Jerusalem,
So famous in song.
Tall cedars of Lebanon
Saw them pass by;
Under Hebron's cool palms,
Beneath the night sky,
Their tents were oft pitched,
Or where o'er and o'er
Gennesaret's blue waters
Roll up on the shore;
Where Jordan flows onward
To meet this fair sea,
Over Bethlehem's hills,
Through Gethsemane,
The highest, the lowest,
The statesman, the priest,
To Jerusalem came
To keep this great feast;
And there on the hillsides

Beneath the green shade
Of booths, seven days
They their offerings made.

They gave to Jehovah
Their first ripened shocks,
And laid on His altars
The first of their flocks,
Their honey, their oil,
The fruits of the vine,
And, a sweet smelling savor —
Their fairest of kine.
'Twas a feast of rejoicing.
And in this solemn way,
The old Hebrews kept
Their Thanksgiving day.

History: Fair Jewess, the feasts
That you held in this way
Built the cradle that rocked
Our Thanksgiving day.
Now, who shall be next?

Spirit: We will cross o'er the sea.
O daughter of England!
Come hither to me.

Harvest Home:

O spirits! I am here at thy command.
What is thy will with me? I prithee
speak!
For time flies swiftly and I may not tarry.

Spirits:
We pray that to us, fair maiden you'll come,
And tell of the feasts in your far English home.

Harvest Home: Alas! the England of to-day belongs not to me; so I'll but tell ye of the sports I looked upon in my youth, that old time when Egbert, and after him great Alfred, ruled over Saxon England. It was then, when we had garnered our grain, that we held our great feast; that old Harvest Home whose sports ceased not till the full moon had passed the meridian. While this feast lasted we held our rude athletic sports on the green, or kindled great bonfires and danced with the maidens who adorned themselves with wreaths of flowers and grains, and as the day waned, we would spread our rustic feasts before the cottage doors, where sat our old men drinking their possets of thickened milk and telling over their tales of the days when Britain was but a vassal of great Rome.

History: Thy feast, Harvest Home,
Was one link in the chain
That made our Thanksgiving.
Now, who comes again?

Spirits: Let us turn from the stories
Of Greece and of Rome,
From the great Jewish feast

And the old Harvest Home,
To our land where the pine-trees
Rose stately and tall,
And o'er bark-covered wigwams
Let long shadows fall;
When all sounds that were heard
Were the birds and the bees,
The ripple of waters,
Or rustling of trees;
When Nature's best gifts
Still in mother-earth slept —

Child: O, how in that time
.Was the festival kept?

Indian: When the frost-spirit came,
And with fingers so cold,
Touched the trees till they blossomed
In red and in gold;
When the wind shook their boughs
Till the ripe nuts dropped down
And the uplands were changing
Their green robes to brown,
Then the sons of the forest,
In festive attire,
Beneath the tall trees
Kindled many a fire;
And, while wild game was roasting
Their bows were unstrung,
The peace-pipe was circling,

And the old and the young
Recounted the brave deeds
Of their sires of old,
And their own feats of daring
Were often retold.

And thus, when the autumn
Was speeding away,
The sons of the forest
Kept their festal day.

History (waves her hand):

O, mists from the past!
Roll backward, and show,
How they kept this
Old festival time, long ago.

TABLEAU II

(A wigwam covered with blankets or fur rugs;
Indians seated around a fire in the centre, smoking
the pipe of peace. The fire, as in the preceding tableau, may be of burning alcohol. Conceal the dish
containing the alcohol with sticks of wood or
branches of trees.)

Now, shadow of days
That were long since o'er,
Return to your place
In the old past, once more.

(To audience:)

          And ye who are listening
          Behold in what way
          These old nations kept
          Their Thanksgiving day,
          But the *real* Thanksgiving
          Dates back to that time
          When the Mayflower came
          ' Mid the snow and the rime.

(To spirits:)

          O spirits! once more
          I pray you draw near
          And bid that first
          Thanksgiving day now appear.

Spirits: Before thee, O History!
          All lowly we bow.
          Thy call we have heard
          And thy work we'll do now;
          So, come, we are calling,
          Thou Thanksgiving day.
          Draw near now, and tell
          Of the old times, we pray.

Thanksgiving (comes forward):

          Shall I tell you the story
          Of those days of woe,
          When we laid half our number
          Beneath the cold snow?

When the heart in each bosom
Was fainting with dread
And none dared even weep
O'er the graves of the dead?
But we levelled them all
Lest the foe, counting o'er,
Should know when grim death
Had knocked at the door.

History:
Yes, that is the story we want, so proceed;
Tell us, how was first planted this Thanks-
giving seed.

Thanksgiving: You know full well the story
of the sad winter of 1621.
You have read how bravely we endured cold,
hunger, the fear of cruel savages, and the sickness that sent half our number to the grave.

Child: And what ' came of the rest?
Tell the story to me.
Did they sail back again
To their homes o'er the sea?

Thanksgiving: Nay, child! the God we
served gave us strength to endure all our trials,
and made the wily savages our friends. At last
the winter was over, and when the oak-leaves
were as big as a mouse's ear we planted our
seeds — corn, barley, and peas.

Child: Were these all?

Thanksgiving: Each family had its vege-
table garden near the house, but these were our
grains; and, so great was the harvest God gave
us, that Governor Bradford set apart a day of
Thanksgiving for the mercies vouchsafed to us.
That was a busy time in Plymouth town.   For
some did shoulder their matchlocks and scour
the woods, from whence they brought a goodly
store of venison and wild fowl.   Others, with
their fishing tackle, brought us of the best of
the sea and the brooks, so we had no lack of
meat.

Our grapes were as sweet and purple as those
of Eshcol, and our pumpkins lay like balls of
gold amid the brown stubble of the cornfields,
and beneath the forest trees the nuts were to
be had for the gathering.

'Twas a wondrous feast, and Massasoit and
ninety of his Indian warriors came to help us
keep it.

We set before them the best of our larders,
and entertained them with games and military
movements.   Then, when three days had
passed, we sent them to their homes, well
pleased with the " white-man's feast," and this
was the way we kept the first Thanksgiving day.

History: Now appear unto us,
            Thou shade of that day,

Let now these thy children
Behold thee at play.

TABLEAU III

(Puritans and Indians at the table; all have eyes
raised and hands clasped as if in prayer, while distant voices sing one or more verses of "America.")

History: Let the mists from the past
Now once more arise,
And cover this Thanksgiving
Scene from our eyes;
Then, let other Thanksgivings
Appear unto me.

Spirit: Well, here is the next one,
In sixteen-twenty-three.

Child: And why was that kept?

Spirit: Because scorched and dry
Grew the earth, with no rain
From May till July.
The ground was all parched,
Like a furnace, the air;
So we turned to our God
And, in fasting and prayer,
We begged He would gather
The clouds in His hand

And scatter the drops
O'er our famishing land.

Child: Did He hear?

Spirits: Aye, He heard
And ere the night came
The warm rain was falling;
And so, in His name,
To give thanks to the One
Who revived the dry earth,
This second Thanksgiving day
Then had its birth.

Child: Were there other Thanksgivings?

Spirits: O yes, many more,
Thanksgivings for peace
And blessings galore;
For victories won,
For enemies slain,
For battles, for harvests
Of ripening grain.
Whatever the blessings,
You see, 'twas their way
To acknowledge them all
By a Thanksgiving day.
And now every year
Since eighteen-sixty-three,
When November appears,

A Thanksgiving you see.
It is always a season
Of pleasure and rest,
When the friends who, like the bird-
     lings.
Have flown from the nest,
Now come fluttering back,
And the years fall away
Till they're children again,
Just for Thanksgiving day.

History: You've been told how the first
Thanksgiving begun,
And was handed along
From the sire to son;
How the threads that were gathered
In west and in east
Were woven to make up
Our Puritan feast,
With old legends and customs
The warp was inlaid.
The woof was the toils
And each sacrifice made
By the people, who, sailing
The wintry sea o'er,
Had builded their homes
On this wild, western shore.
And they bid you for blessings
That One up in heaven,
In mercy and love,

Hath to all of you given,
That, as Thanksgiving
Comes to you every year,
You give to Him glory
For Thanksgiving cheer.

(All step to front of stage, clasp hands, and look up. Recite or sing:)

(Air: " Gaily the Troubadour.")
O, Thou who holdeth safe,
The earth in Thy hand,
Look in Thy mercy now
On our fair land.

May we all ever walk,
Lord, in Thy way;
Honor and ever keep,
Thanksgiving day.

For summer's bloom and autumn's blight.
For bending wheat and blasted maize,
For health and sickness, Lord of light,
And Lord of darkness, hear our praise.
J. G. Holland.

O favors, every year made new!
O gifts, with rain and sunshine sent!
The bounty overruns our due,
The fulness shames our discontent.

God gives us with our rugged soil
  The power to make it Eden-fair,
And richer fruits to crown our toil,
  Than summer-wedded islands bear.

J. G. Whittier.

THE END.